The Theatre Careers Handbook 2013

a (pro) directory

© Stage Jobs Pro 2012

First edition published 2012 by

Stage Jobs Pro
131/132 Upper Street
Islington
London N1 1QP

www.stagejobspro.com

A CIP catalogue record for this book is available from the British Library

ISBN 978-0-9556273-9-2

Set in Frutiger & Serifa
Designed and produced by Prepare to Publish Ltd
(www.preparetopublish.com)

Every effort has been made to ensure accuracy but the publishers and editor
cannot accept any legal responsibility for errors or omissions.

Printed in Britain by
Polestar Wheatons, Exeter

Acknowledgements

We are very grateful to the following people and organisations for their contributions to this book. Their insight and advice is invaluable to those starting out in theatre. Many thanks are due to:

- Julie Alchin & Huw Morgan, Get Into Theatre – **www.getintotheatre.org**
- Cathy Thomas & Amelia Forsbrook, IdeasTap – **www.ideastap.com**
- Vanessa Jones, Julian Caddy & Rachel Strange, Brighton Fringe – **www.brightonfringe.org**
- Robert West, Creative & Cultural Skills – **www.ccskills.org.uk**
- The HR Department, Ambassador Theatre Group – **www.atgtickets.com**
- Simon Lovelace, Crew Class – **www.crewclass.co.uk**
- Sandra Exelby & Caroline Silk, National Association of Screen Make-up Artists and Hairdressers – **www.nasmah.co.uk**
- Natalie Brown, London College of Fashion – **www.fashion.arts.ac.uk**
- Martha Gall, Stage Technologies – **www.stagetech.com**
- Shadia Fakhoury & Robin Townley, Association of British Theatre Technicians – **www.abtt.org.uk**
- Andy Rowley, Stage Management Association – **www.stagemanagementassociation.co.uk**
- Ian Saunders, Association of Lighting Designers – **www.ald.org.uk**
- Gareth Fry, Association of Sound Designers – **www.associationofsounddesigners.com**
- Anna Edgar

And lastly, a big thank you to the Stage Jobs Pro members who kindly shared their experience, talent and advice with the next generation of theatre professionals.

If you have any questions about this book or feel an organisation or company ought to be included in future editions please send details to info@blue-compass.com.

Introduction

Do you love the thrill of live theatre? The excited chatter of the audience, the expectant hush that descends as the lights dim, and that marvellous moment when the curtain rises and the performance begins... Or do you prefer live music? Or live events?

You don't need to be an actor, singer or dancer to play a vital part in making these productions happen. If you're prepared for long hours and hard work – there's no 9 to 5 in theatreland – a career in theatre can be incredibly rewarding and fulfilling.

You could be working in a receiving theatre, or with one of the touring companies that visit them for a short time as part of their touring schedule. You could be part of a producing theatre where productions are developed in house. If you're working for a larger company you might get the chance to travel across the world with your show.

One month you could be working on a summertime open air Shakespeare play in the sun (or rain...!), and the next you might be turning your attention to a site-specific production in a more unusual venue such as the Old Vic Tunnels.

Theatre offers the chance for a career that you control: you can work freelance on lots of different productions, or take on a single long-term contract if you prefer the stability of permanent work. There are many different pathways you can take, with lots of opportunity for progression – and diversion – to take on new responsibilities and challenges as you build up your skills and experience.

If you're interested in the technical side of things you could be designing and implementing a lighting scheme that enhances the themes and moods of the piece, or making sure the sound levels in the performance are at their optimum for the audience's enjoyment. You could even be a part of the Automation department – an exciting new area of theatre common on largescale and big touring productions.

Those of an artistic bent can design costumes, or create incredible effects on the actors with prosthetics and make-up. You could plan and build set and scenery, or source the perfect props. You could be the one directing the performance, bringing a script to life with a group of actors.

There's the Stage Management team who call the shots backstage, bringing these different departments together to make sure each production runs smoothly and to the highest standard.

Or you could be working in theatre management itself: in the administration department; helping to promote and market productions; overseeing the ushers and box office activities in Front of House; or choosing and programming the perfect shows for your venue's Spring, Summer, Autumn or Winter season.

Here at Stage Jobs Pro we're passionate about making the life of theatre professionals that little bit easier, and about informing people like you about the exciting possibilities a career in theatre can offer. This book is intended as a guide to the industry: the different roles that are available and where they sit on a career ladder; where to go for training and advice on how to fund it; the vital organisations you need to know about; advice on applying for work experience and jobs, and articles on key elements of the theatre world.

We've included case studies and personal advice from our members – the people who are out there working in the industry right now – with information on how they got to where they are now, and where they plan to go next.

There's also a glossary in the final chapter for you to look up any words or technical terms you do not recognise.

The Theatre Careers Handbook is brought to you by the UK's central networking and recruitment resource for theatre professionals. **www.stagejobspro.com/uk**

Chapter 1
Job Types

Backstage

There is a very wide range of different roles available backstage, from Sound and Lighting, to Stage Management and Wardrobe. We've listed the most common roles, the responsibilities associated with that role and where the role sits on the career ladder for that area of backstage work. Also included are some great Q&As with Stage Jobs Pro members who are working in these posts to give you some insight into how they got there, and where they're going next.

At the end of each listing are helpful organisations, unions, books and some of the courses available in the UK. These lists are by no means exhaustive and it's worth using the Internet to research what courses are run in your local area and check their current pricings and schedules.

Lighting

Lighting Technician

Lighting Technicians work with the Lighting Designer to implement the lighting scheme for a performance. They are responsible for maintaining and operating lighting equipment, programming the LX desk, and doing paperwork. Lighting Technicians often begin their careers by working as apprentice lighting technicians or lighting assistants, and can progress to the position of Deputy Chief Electrician or Chief Electrician.

Lighting Designer

Lighting Designers are responsible for the creative side of lighting – they design the lighting plot for performances, often working with the Lighting Technician to realise their designs. They can become Deputy Chief Electrician or Chief Electrician.

Stage Jobs Pro member Declan Randall is a Lighting Designer. We asked him the following questions about his career:

What is the most rewarding aspect of working as a Lighting Designer?
I think that one of the primary reasons that I do what I do is because I love being a part of the "story-telling" process that is theatre. Being able to manipulate the medium which is light and use that to enhance the mood, support emotions, even trick the audience into seeing things in a certain way is great fun. It also means that I hardly ever have to wear a suit and tie!

What are the key skills required to be an effective Lighting Designer?
Being a lighting designer you are part scientist, part technician, part artist, part psychologist. Lighting design for me is a fusion of all these parts. You have to have an artistic flair, but you also have to have a good understanding of what is required technically to see it through and realise your ideas. You have to be a 'people person' and good communication skills are essential.

Do you see your role as a natural step on a career ladder, and if so what is the next rung?
I could move on from being an LD and go into production management, or technical direction, but I love what I do, so for me, I am on my top rung.

How did you work your way into your current role?
I studied lighting and started out working as a technician in several theatres. It's the best way to learn – you get to meet other designers, you learn from them and slowly you start to develop your own ideas on what works and what doesn't and it kind of happened from there. It was a process – I did not just wake up one day and say "hey, I'm a lighting designer". It was years of hard work and relationship building.

How much do you think networking helps towards landing a job in the industry?
Networking is always important – you never know where your next job will come from, so talk to everyone and anyone. You never know who will "know someone who knows someone who's looking for someone."

Do you think you will be working in the industry in the next five years, and if so in what capacity?
I hope to be working in the industry for the next 50 years, ok, well the next 30 at least and hopefully always as a lighting designer. I can't help it – I love what I do.

Please describe what a typical day working as a Lighting Designer might contain?
This depends. It is really dependant on what stage of the process you are in. Some days you might have to be

in rehearsals, others you might be sitting at home (or in the office) drawing the lighting plan, but once you move into the theatre, be prepared for long days (14 to 18 hours are not uncommon) where you will need to be – and be expected to be – alert and concentrating. You will start with a focus session in the morning, then have a rehearsal on stage in the afternoon and then start programming/plotting that night.

Have you done any additional training courses to further your career?
I studied lighting and lighting design, but I think that if I was to study further, some sort of personnel management course, or business management courses would be good. It's good and helpful to know your way around the computer, so perhaps courses in PhotoShop or CAD are good to do too.

How important is working for free at the beginning of your career?
I still work for free every now and then! I am not sure that you should be working for free as a means to build your career – I think that you should work for free if you truly believe in a project and want to give something back to the industry. You never know where the next piece of theatrical gem will come from, so sometimes you agree to "help out" and who knows – it might be your best work ever.

Declan also wrote this great article for the Association of Lighting Designers. It's a brilliant insight into the process of devising and implementing a lighting scheme that really matches his description of the Lighting Designer as 'part scientist, part technician, part artist, part psychologist':

Dialogues with Light – by Declan Randall

LIGHTING POULENC'S "DIALOGUES DES CARMELITES" AT GUILDHALL SCHOOL OF MUSIC AND DRAMA

The opera is based on a true story – it's about the persecution of the Carmelite nuns during the French Revolution. It's not a happy story, as you can imagine, as so few true stories that become operas are.

The plot revolves around a central (fictional) character called Blanche who is born into the world in fear and seems to grow up to be someone who is always afraid. It was this shattered psyche and the opening scene where her carriage is attacked and the windows smashed that gave set designer David Farley the starting point for his marvellous design. The show opens with a projected image of the

"As with any good piece of theatrical writing, light is inherent to the telling of the story"

shattering glass (one which we used again, both as a negative image and later, red with blood) which were designed by final year student Chris Jackson. Both director Stephen Barlow and David wanted the stage to feel closed in and almost threatening and offer the audience a sense of the danger and fear that ruled Blanche's life. This was achieved by two sets of sliders and headers, shaped like fragments of the shattered glass, which would move in and out to open up and close down the space and create the location for the many different locations within the opera. The main performance area was a raked wedge which revolved as required to further change the location settings. I fell in love with the set the first time I saw it and knew how important the light would be that helped to enhance the sense of fear and dread that Blanche felt and that the set created – and I just could not wait to get "stuck in".

Most of the scenes called for a specific light source, and even if these were not actually seen, they were certainly alluded to. As with any good piece of theatrical writing, light is inherent to the telling of the story. It is written that it gets darker and more ominous which adds to her fear and flickering candlelight would cast shadows on the walls which would frighten her. Daylight and candlelight became the two main motivating light sources, but as she (Blanche) was living in a world that to her was full of fear, I did not want to use colours that were too realistic in suggesting the motivating

light. For instance, I wanted daylight, but it needed to be an uncomfortable daylight – something that was just "off-normal" and unsettling. The same applied to the candlelight – it was warm and flickering – but it was not a 'happy' or a 'cosy' warm. The other dictating factor about the light that Blanche's world demanded was that it was fractured and broken. This again, ties in with the theme of the broken glass that is established early on in the opera. There were a number of cues that we created for Blanche that would slowly fade in a gobo wash as she entered the scene, so that it was almost as if her mere presence was causing the light to fracture and break. Depending on the tone of the scene, these were then adjusted in intensity to become more dominant as her fear grew and then would recede slightly as she was comforted, but never going away completely.

I love colour. It excites me and is what draws me to lighting design. Choosing the colour palette for Blanche's world was indeed a challenge. My starting point was the broken glass. I thought about the colours that clear glass refracts when shattered – the greens, yellows and blues and took it from there. The trick was that Blanche, whilst being the central character, was not the only character, and so the colour choice had to also work and be believable in the worlds of the other characters too. I ended up choosing a range of colours that all tended to the greener side of the spectrum, as this was the dominant colour in my 'broken glass' approach. For this, I found that the steel greens, green tints as well as the sodiums and mustards were very effective. Few of the colours were very saturated – the costumes were true to the period and nun's habits are shades of black brown, both of which need a fair amount of light to 'read' on stage.

Textured light was also a huge part of the lighting design and a big part of Blanche's world. Few of the gobos were ever in sharp focus though, unless they were depicting a window or other locational device. I opted for a "just-off-sharp" edge and often combined this with a split-colour gel to add to the sense of the 'shattered light'. Linear break-ups were heavily used which helped to create the illusion of the light filtering through the broken timber or boarded up windows.

As is the case with any production, it simply cannot be done without the teamwork, effort and dedication of the crew. The team at Guildhall are fantastic – from the staff to the students. There is a huge amount of talent being nurtured there, from the singers to the orchestra and the stage team and technicians. Nothing was ever too much trouble and everything was carried out with the highest standards of professionalism and care.

The end of the opera is perhaps one of the most well-known with the 15 nuns being executed one by one while they sing the Salve Regina, their voices dropping out one at a time as the blade falls. We decided that instead of going the obvious route of taking lights out on each nun as they died, we decided to add light to each of them. A carefully focussed backlight and uplight was added in as each nun dies. Blanche runs in to join her sisters in their sentence, and as the last blade falls we opened up the stage, pulling out all the headers and sliders and opening up the

cyclorama which faded up to a bright white using 2 x 2.5kw HMI Fresnels to achieve this. This 'white-out' echoed the sense of the release that she felt from her world and fear of life.

Sorry, but I could hardly write about the Carmelite nuns without at least one nun joke creeping in. I know, it's a bad habit...

This article was reproduced in its entirety with kind permission by Declan Randall. Declan's website is **www.declanrandall.com**.

How to be a Lighting Designer

THIS GUIDE WAS WRITTEN BY THE ASSOCIATION OF LIGHTING DESIGNERS

The Association of Lighting Designers

Below are some suggestions and advice on how to go about being a lighting designer! Life is obviously not quite that simple, but hopefully it will give you some idea of the various options and choices you can make. This is a fairly personal view and obviously every lighting designer will have have their own view on the best way into the profession.

Firstly, you don't really need a qualification to be a lighting designer – experience is what really counts and you may have already started gaining that from amateur or school productions. You can add to that by getting involved with local youth theatre groups or other amateur companies, it's all about being able to show a commitment and enthusiasm.

There are a few ways into theatre. You can pester every theatre company you can find until they give you a job. It might be sweeping the stage or follow spot operator for panto but it's a way in and then you can gradually work your way up. It's slow and you only gain a limited amount of experience at a time, but it works for some people.

"Experience is what really counts and you may have already started gaining that from amateur or school productions"

Or you can continue with your studies through A levels and on to university – studying whatever interests you, but also getting involved with any drama or musical or dance groups that are going on there. Many universities do drama courses, but they tend to be fairly general and I'm not aware of any that do a Lighting Design course. However, many universities have good resources and you will make a lot of contacts – plus you come out of it with a qualification, so if you do decide that theatre, or lighting design specifically, is not for you, you have something to fall back on.

Another form of further education is training at drama school. They generally take on students from about 18 years, though they may consider someone younger. The courses cover all aspects of backstage theatre and most last three years, but you will come out of it with good contacts and a good chance of getting work. There are one or two colleges that offer a degree course in Lighting Design. Drama schools offer a good training in how to put on a production and you will get plenty of opportunities to put what you learn into practice in a working theatre environment.

Not many lighting designers have come into the business as lighting designers, generally they have moved on from theatre electricians where they gain the knowledge and understanding of the practical side of lighting design. It is also very difficult to earn a living solely as a lighting designer, most of us supplement our income with other technical work. But, times are changing and it is now possible to train as a lighting designer which means that if you have the contacts and some experience you can make a career (and a living) as a lighting designer without working through the industry as we had to in the past.

Don't forget there are other parts of the entertainment industry that use lighting designers – television, film, music, corporate presentations, industry launches, architecture, theme parks, museums, retail... and what you need to do is find your niche and go for it.

However it is important to keep studying if you are still at school or college (a few extra GCSEs and A levels won't do any harm) and gain as much experience as you can. Please feel free to get in touch if you need any more help.

Top Tips for Aspiring Lighting Designers:

• It's all about experience – what you've seen and what you've done. See as much performance as possible and be inspired.

• Consider all aspects of lighting design. This article concentrates on theatrical lighting (which includes opera, musicals, dance etc), but there are also concerts, television, architecture, shops, product launches etc.

• Learn what everyone else on the production team does and how they do it. The production will be at its best if everyone contributes rather than contradicts, the lighting design should complement and enhance the production.

• The traditional way to a career as a lighting designer is to work your way up through the electrical department of a theatre and then take on the occasional design, all the while gaining more experience. There is no reason why this experience shouldn't start at school, college or your local amateur company.

Job Types

- Lighting design now forms a part of most drama school technical/backstage theatre courses. These courses cover all aspects of backstage work and you can then specialise in the final year of the course. Check the college curriculum for more details and it can be helpful to ask the college to put you in touch with current and past students so you can get a student's perspective on what the course has to offer.
- It is now possible to train as a lighting designer on a specific course, at a drama college or university. These are often degree courses and last 2 or 3 years. However, don't expect to walk out of the course and straight into the next big West End musical, you will still need to gain professional experience.
- Discover, and attach yourself to, the next generation of set designers and directors. This can be easier if you are at college with them. Many directors and designers prefer to work with people they know and if they make it to the top they can take you with them.
- The theatre and performance industry is about reputation. Everyone talks about and remembers a good production (small or large scale) and many successful lighting designers have made their name by being part of just one or two outstanding productions. It can work the other way too though!
- Only those at the top of the profession can earn a living just from lighting design. Be prepared to supplement your income with other freelance work within the industry, for example fit-ups, followspot work, lighting desk operator. But you can use this as an opportunity to see other lighting designers at work.
- Finally, try and meet other lighting designers and consider joining an association (ALD – Association of Lighting Designers or ABTT – Association of British Theatre Technicians). They can offer you valuable advice and help and then point you in the right direction.

This guide has been reproduced with kind permission from the Association of Lighting Designers. The Association of Lighting Designers is a professional body representing lighting designers working in the live performance industry in the United Kingdom and many other parts of the world: www.ald.org.uk

Lighting Operator

Lighting Operators will set up and prepare lighting equipment before a performance, as well as operating the LX desk during it following the cues from the Stage Manager or Deputy Stage Manager. A Lighting Operator may move on to work as a Lighting Technician, Deputy Chief Electrician or Chief Electrician.

Electrician

The Electrician works to realise the lighting designs, usually on largescale productions. They are responsible for rigging, rewiring, and may also, in touring productions, be responsible for get ins and get outs. Electricians can progress to take on the role of Deputy Chief Electrician, or Chief Electrician.

Chief Electrician

The Chief Electrician is the Head of the Lighting department and is usually permanently employed by the theatre.

Followspot Operator (Spotlight Operator)

Followspot Operator is very often the first step in getting into theatre lighting. Followspot Operators move a spotlight to follow an actor onstage. A Followspot Operator may move up the LX department ladder to become a Lighting Operator or Lighting Designer.

USEFUL ORGANISATIONS

The Association of Lighting Designers – *www.ald.org.uk*
The International Association of Lighting Designers – *www.iald.org*
The Association of British Theatre Technicians – *www.abtt.org.uk*

BOOKS ON LIGHTING

Stage Lighting – The Technician's Guide, Skip Mort, 2011
Lighting and Sound, Neil Fraser, 1993
Basics – A Beginner's Guide To Stage Lighting, Peter Coleman, 2003
The Stage Guide to working in Lighting and Sound, Geoffrey Joyce, 2008

LIGHTING COURSES IN THE UK

Entertainment & Theatre Electrician – City & Guild
www.qurl.com/cityguild
BA (Hons) Stage Electrics and Lighting Design – Royal Academy of
Dramatic Art
www.qurl.com/radaseld
PG Dip Stage Electrics and Lighting Design – Royal Academy of Dramatic Art
www.qurl.com/radapgdip
Lighting Design for the Theatre – Royal Academy of Dramatic Art
www.qurl.com/radald
BA (Hons) Theatre Practice Theatre Lighting Design – Centre School of
Speech & Drama
www.qurl.com/cssdld
BA (Hons) Theatre Practice Production Lighting – Centre School of Speech
& Drama
www.qurl.com/cssdpl
Lighting & Sound Production (Foundation Degree) – Northbrook College
www.qurl.com/northcol
BA (Hons) Lighting Design – Rose Bruford College
www.qurl.com/rosebruld
BA (Hons) Creative Lighting Control – Rose Bruford College
www.qurl.com/rosebrulc
Sound & Lighting for Beginners – Activate
www.qurl.com/activsl
Advanced Sound & Lighting – Activate
www.qurl.com/activtt

Sound

Careers in Theatre Sound

THIS GUIDE WAS KINDLY WRITTEN BY GARETH FRY AT THE ASSOCIATION OF SOUND DESIGNERS

ASSOCIATION *of* SOUND DESIGNERS

Speak to more than a couple of people working in theatre sound and in all likelihood they all came into the industry via different routes. Some people start off in theatre working across a number of disciplines and end up specialising in sound; others start in other parts of the sound industry and move into theatre. As with many jobs in this handbook, there are a few key job titles in use, but the exact job descriptions often vary considerably according to the genre and needs of a specific production; the venue it is playing in, or the venues it may tour to, whether national or internationally; whether there is an in-house sound system or not; and the scale of the production. Given that there is no norm, we felt it would be interesting to tell you a bit about the job titles and then hear from some of the people doing those jobs and how they got there.

Sound Designer – will work with a director and producer to create a sound system and the sounds going through it to meet the specific demands of a show. A much longer description of this role can be found on the Association of Sound Designers' website: **www.associationofsounddesigners.com**

Production Sound Engineer – will work with the sound designer to realise the sound system practically.

Sound Operator – typically the term Sound Op' is used for sound engineers working on plays. The Sound Op' will be at each performance of the show and will play the sound effects into the show at the appropriate cue points.

No.1 Sound – typically the term No.1 Sound is used for sound engineers working on musicals. The No.1 sound will be at each performance of the play and mix all the microphones and play the sound effects from the FOH mixing desk.

"Wherever you start, you're in for a lifetime of learning, as new technologies are adopted rapidly and diversely"

21

No.2 Sound – the No.2 is often responsible for the onstage side of the sound for a musical. This will often be the radio mics that the performers are wearing and the band. They will also mix the show as cover to the No.1.

No.3/Radio Mic Technician – Typically responsible for the radio mics, which involve a lot of maintenance, and liaising with the cast wearing them, which involves a lot of sweaty backs! Setting up the radio mics on a show is a highly skilled job requiring the skill to be able to diagnose the myriad technical faults that can occur with them, to deal with a variety of wardrobe and dressing scenarios, and immense people skills to bring the performers on side so they perform with their radio mics as constructively as possible.

These job titles are most often found in the freelance world: working full time in a venue might mean that at various points you may have to move between any, or all of the above roles. There are a variety of other roles found in theatre sound, and countless others working for equipment manufacturers, distributors, installers and hire companies.

There are a few formal training routes into theatre sound – many people train at drama schools on a variety of stage management and technical theatre courses. Central School of Speech and Drama, RADA and Rose Bruford offer specialist theatre sound courses. There are a variety of other courses that offer specialised training in sound, often with a focus towards music recording and production, and consequently don't provide training in the specifics of making work for theatre. Nonetheless, a lot of people working in theatre started off somewhere else and learnt on the job – with the pace of technological development, wherever you start, you're in for a lifetime of learning, as new technologies are adopted rapidly and diversely.

The Association of Sound Designers represents the interests of sound designers in the UK theatre industry: **www.associationofsounddesigners.com**. In addition to writing the above guide they have also included Q&As with some of their members who are working in diverse sound roles across the industry for this chapter.

Sound Technician / Sound Engineer

The Sound Technician will test and maintain equipment, set up sound equipment, run sound checks and often run the sound during performances, and will then pack away all the equipment after the performance.

Stage Jobs Pro member Jamie Parker is a Sound Technician. We asked him the following questions about his career:

What is the most rewarding aspect of working as a Sound Technician?
Achieving a good, solid mix. There are lots of factors to what we do, but the end result is one thing only, and that is for as many people in the audience as possible to hear a good version of what is happening on the stage.

What are the key skills required to be an effective Sound Technician?
Good ears, first and foremost. It's all very well learning equations and how to use the latest piece of gear, but actually making sure it sounds good is far more important than all of that. Interpersonal skills are very important; if the performer or client doesn't like you or doesn't feel safe, you've lost the gig. Being head-strong and independent goes a long way.

Do you see your role as a natural step on a career ladder, and if so what is the next rung?
Perhaps, but this industry is quite vague in terms of career progression. I see it more as 'which direction will I turn at the next roundabout'. It's all about grasping opportunity and being aware of where the industry itself is heading.

How did you work your way into your current role?
My most recent contract was with Rambert Dance Company as Sound Engineer for their Autumn/Spring Tours 12/13. To secure that, I had to have previous touring experience, which I had through touring with the Harlem Gospel Choir, and numerous lower-profile theatre tours. Previous to that, I had a multitude of roles, each bringing their own bits of experience, from corporate work to cruise ships to studio recording – it's funny how skills learnt along the way can suddenly be useful later in your career.

How much do you think networking helps towards landing a job in the industry?
A lot! If nobody knows who you are, you're not going anywhere. You need to be proactive, outgoing, and in the right place at the right time (which isn't a mystical art – see what's happening and be there!). Also, this is very much an industry that works on who employers like working with, rather than who has the 'best CV'. If they like you, you're in. Simple.

Do you think you will be working in the industry in the next five years, and if so in what capacity?
Yes of course. As previously stated, I think trying to foreplan a career path in this industry is asking for trouble. I intend to keep seeing where work is available, and following that path. The industry is always changing – previous safe paths are now almost closed off, and new, never foreseen

paths are opening up. Be vigilant and aware. Long term career plans are asking for disappointment as a sound technician.

Please describe what a typical day working as a Sound Technician might contain?

'Typical day' is a bit difficult to define in this career. However, in my most recent role on tour with the RDC, we meet the trucks at the theatre on day 1, unload and I start rigging the sound system with my allocated crew, finishing at about 10pm. Day 2 is another early start for checks, run-throughs and first performances. The rest of the week is more relaxed, with later starts unless we have matinees. Then after the last show, we derig and generally shut the last truck at about 3am. Of course, a 'typical day' varies massively across the industry. Only key rule: be flexible, and forget any idea of 9-5!

Have you done any additional training courses to further your career?

Aside from a training day from Midas on their Pro-series digital desks, all my training outside of my diploma and degree has been on-the-job. However, I can see at some point in the future, specific training would be useful. Currently, health and safety is a big one to have, especially for bigger venues. And other courses to broaden my knowledge – rigging for example is often useful.

Question 9: How important is working for free at the beginning of your career?

I'd never do this, and think it is a bad thing for anyone to do. It harms the industry greatly – of course companies will abuse free labour, in favor sometimes of more skilled paid labour. I've seen it happen over and over. If you're in the industry, even at the beginning, you're still worth money. Don't accept 'but we're training you' or 'we'll start to pay you soon'. If you're there, you're worth money. And there are companies who will pay – keep searching.

Jamie's website is **www.jamie-parker.com**

David Gregory is a Production Sound Engineer. His recent projects include Propeller's Taming of the Shrew and Twelfth Night world tour.

What does your job entail?

My job entails working with a sound designer to get the best combination of equipment for a production with the budget available, the time and staff available, which meets the needs of the show and the designer. Then I work out how that equipment is linked together and becomes a complete sound system, the correct cables, A-D converters, microphones, clips, stands and how to install the show into the venue in the most efficient way possible, such as how the speakers can be rigged where the designer wants them, in a safe way. Essentially I look after the practical side of a production's audio requirements.

What's a typical day for you?

I'm freelance, and tend to work about 60 hours a week. I typically start work in the morning at a venue, wherever that might be in the country and work till 10:45pm. There tends to be four phases to each job – planning, the fit up, the tech and previews. Most jobs last 7 to 12 days on site and pay tends to be £225 per day.

How did you get to where you are now?

I worked as an apprentice to a company for four years, and also shadowed a lot of people, which was valuable to gain the experience needed to start to talk to designers and engineers in the correct way.

What training exists to become a production sound engineer?

There are some great audio engineering courses out there. I have read about City and Guilds courses. Also there are theatre design courses such as Central School of Speech and Drama. I would say the best form of training for production sound is on the job. Working in a hires warehouse can be a great place to get familiar with the equipment you are going to use, and also the people who will hopefully be your colleagues. I'm a person who learns from reading; John Leonard's "Theatre Sound" book is a good read. And also Yamaha's "Sound Reinforcement Handbook" is a great reference guide.

What's the best thing about your job?

The variety – each production and venue throws up different challenges.

What is the most challenging aspect of your job?

The technology we use in our industry is rapidly changing, our field is growing in size and standards are getting higher. Also, making productions happen with limited resources. Obtaining money for proper staffing is harder than obtaining money for equipment.

David is a member of the Assocation of Sound Designers. Interview reproduced in its entirety with kind permission from the Association.

Sound Designer

Sound Designers work to create a soundscape that enhances the production. They are responsible for both managerial and artistic tasks, such as developing the sound plan with the Director, but also for practical tasks – recording and manipulating sound files and tracks.

Emma Laxton is a Sound Designer. Her recent projects include The Physicists (Donmar), The Sacred Flame (ETT).

What's a typical day for you?

During the rehearsal phase of a show, I'll spend time in rehearsals watching, going to production meetings, organising hires, making sounds, and talking with the director. I'll make the sounds for a show either in the rehearsal room, at home, in a studio or in the theatre. During the production weeks I'll be at the theatre 10 am– 10pm, though I may also have another show in rehearsal that will need attention – I have two shows in rehearsal at the moment. My job tends to be 7 days a week, and often will involve working through holidays and fielding calls and requests from directors at all hours.

How did you get to where you are now?

I did work experience at my local theatre in Shrewsbury, and I got a followspot op job there from that and eventually became the technical manager! I went to Central School and did the Stage Management and Technical Arts course, I hadn't done any sound before but I realised the whole point of going to drama school is to learn the bits you don't know and to find out what you're interested in, so I chose to sound for a term and really enjoyed that. I stayed on for another year to do the BA Theatre Studies final year and did a lot of work placements at Les Mis, Miss Saigon and the Royal Albert Hall. My tutor, Ross Brown, put me up for a sound op'ing job at the Royal Court– just a week long job – then they needed someone for the next show, and so on and eventually I became deputy head of sound there. I got an opportunity to design a show upstairs which was a safe environment to start in, and got to do more and more designs there. Eventually I decided that was what I wanted to do, so I went freelance.

How did your training help you?

There are working practises and a language of talking that I learnt at drama school. It's been so useful to me as a sound designer to have been a sound op, an engineer, to have installed sound systems and put radio mics on actors, because I know what I'm asking for. You're always learning on the job and you have to continuously adapt because different directors work in different ways and require different things from you.

What is the most challenging aspect of your job?

It's not the design aspect of things – it's fighting my corner, whether that be the budget or staffing, or to educate the other people you're working with as to your value in the room and your needs to put equipment in the set or auditorium.

Are you freelance, or employed?

I'm freelance, and most of the time I love it – the variety of venues, people and challenges – but it is tough, for example, if you injure yourself and you can't work. There's also the insecurity waiting for your diary to fill up with bookings.

What is the average pay?

I get paid a fee for a production, which often varies between £1k and £4k; this is for plays. You are asked to commit non-exclusively to the rehearsal period, which can often be four to five weeks long, and exclusively for the two production weeks. How much you need to be in rehearsals depends on the job and the director. Musical work pays more and more often pays royalties, but tends to involve longer production periods.

What has been your favourite project to work on, and why?

Invisible for Transport, because of who they are and the work they

want to create. I spent a lot of time in rehearsals and really felt like being part of the company. They had a great attitude towards the way a piece of work evolved on the road and employing the right people to make that happen. The sound was integrated into the show from a really early stage and that really paid off.

What advice would you give for someone wanting to be a sound designer?

Take any little opportunities that come up: readings, studio shows, fringe shows. The associate directors that I worked with at the Court have become the next generation of directors and those contacts have proved great. The fringe shows are great – the limits they place on you make you think really hard about how to do things.

It's often directors that take you places; or set designers, who get brought into a project earlier than anyone else. It's all about networking and meeting people, and at the early stages it's not necessarily about your body of work, as much as about your ability to be part of a team and work well with people. You have to be able to talk to a director. Knowing QLab inside out is essential.

Emma is a member of the Assocation of Sound Designers. Interview reproduced in its entirety with kind permission from the Association.

Job Types

Sound Operator

Sound Operators operate the sound desk during the course of the performance following the cues from the Stage Manager or Deputy Stage Manager. They, along with other members of the sound team are responsible for rigging, de-rigging, and running checks on equipment and acoustics.

Peter Eltringham is a Sound Operator. His recent projects include Chariots of Fire.

What's a typical day for you?
Typically I'll arrive at the theatre at 6pm for a 7.45 show. I'll power up, check through the rig and make sure everything is working. This gives me a contingency time of 30-45 minutes in case anything isn't working. Once the show starts I will be playing in sound effects, mixing the occasional radio mic or float mic, which are either cued by the DSM or myself at a musical cue point. I finish as soon as the show has ended and I've powered down.

How did you get to where you are now?
I was interested in live sound when I was younger, but it wasn't until I did a school production of Les Mis that I got into theatre. I did the sound course at Central School of Speech and Drama. I made lots of contacts there, which proved really useful when I graduated – one of which led to doing fit-ups at Hampstead Theatre, where I got to meet lots of sound designers and get my name known. From there I've got jobs as a sound operator, production sound engineer and as associate sound designer on a range of shows.

What's the best training for a Sound Operator?
Sound operating can be quite a simple job on the face of it. But that's only half of it. Usually I am the only sound person in the theatre – a department of one – so when things go wrong, I have to fix it, fast. I have to understand all the bits of kit and how they work together. The last thing anyone wants is for the show to go up late or even be cancelled. You have to have a good foundation in sound and the equipment used. There are lots of courses that provide this, though op'ing a show at a drama school is a good environment to make mistakes without the consequences you'd face in real life. My experience at CSSD was great for learning the fundamentals, and things like the health and safety aspects of the job. But I've picked up so much on the job itself.

What is the most challenging aspect of your job?
Keeping concentration over two or three hundred shows is essential – you can't afford to make mistakes even though you're watching something that you've seen a million

times before. You want to make sure than the 300th performance gets the same level of attention and diligence as the first night.

Are you freelance, or employed?
A lot of operating tends to be on a PAYE basis, particularly in the West End. Some places allow you to invoice, but it can be tedious to produce an invoice every week – which might take a month to be processed and paid – so often it's easier to be PAYE. The pay averages between £575 and £650 per week, before tax, for an 8-show week, Monday to Saturday.

How long does a contract tend to last?
Contracts tend to run from two weeks to a year long – but shows can close at any time and you're often only given two weeks notice.

What advice would you give for someone wanting to become a sound operator?
You need to learn about lots of things that aren't operating to be a good operator! Take any opportunity you get to learn a new skill. Build your contacts – one job will usually lead to another.

What other roles do you do apart from sound op?
Some people just op', and some do other things with their days. I do installation work, production sound engineering, assistant and associate design work and fringe sound designs.

Peter is a member of the Assocation of Sound Designers. Interview reproduced in its entirety with kind permission from the Association.

Job Types

Sound Manager

The Sound Manager is in charge of all aspects of sound in a production, often working with the Sound Designer and Sound Technician. In small companies, they may also rig and run the sound during performances.

Tom Hares is Senior Technician at Sadlers Wells.

What does your job entail?

The company tends to go for staff who can work in more than one role but have people who have specialist skills. So I'm the only 'sound technician' and lead on that but do also assist with flys and sometimes with lighting when appropriate. Our theatre programme is normally a new show each week, normally from outside companies on tour but also in-house productions too. Over Christmas and Summer, we tend to have a show in residence for a few weeks and we'll do a number of one day events and showcases over the year around the normal bookings. I have to ensure that our in-house kit is maintained to a good standard and that I know how to operate it all, check incoming riders and source any kit that we don't have, often liaising with incoming engineers and rental companies to meet each other's requirements. I have to book casual staff to meet any sound team requirements and then lead them from the first day of fit-up to the closing of the doors at the get-out. I have to be available to meet sudden changes in the needs of the show. And I have to assist with the general running of the department.

What's a typical day for you?

Prior to opening night, I will normally be assisting visiting companies sound crew in setting up and preparing their kit and leading any casual sound staff we've employed for the show. During rehearsals, I'll be onstage learning the show. I'm not often at the desk as the visiting engineer will do that but I'm often the Duty Technician for the building – dealing with FOH clearance and any emergencies that should arise during the show (fire alarms and so on). I try and operate a show every so often so that I can keep in practice and I'll often shadow the operator on any show that is playing for a few weeks so that I can be emergency cover. Once the show is up and running, I'll be scheduling sound crew for upcoming shows, sourcing rental kit and generally checking audio requirements for upcoming shows – ideally we like to have the prep work for future shows done with a month in hand.

I also assist our Technical Director with the departmental finances so there will be an office day per week. This office day is sometimes spent on union activities as I'm the site rep and union branch secretary, and probably once a month I'll be offsite. This will either be looking after our offsite storage which I also have control over, or working on a broader project. These have included being part of the working group that revised the National Occupational Standards for Technical Theatre education, keeping up to speed on the 800MHz Clearance.

How did you get to where you are now? Was there (or is there now) training courses available?
I started at my local youth theatre during school holidays. While studying GCSEs I became interested in the technical side of theatre, particular lighting. After A Levels, I studied an HND in Lighting and Sound Design (a course no longer running) and worked alongside at the college theatre which did a fair amount of community theatre, so my paid work was running alongside my learning. I moved to London to study for a degree in Theatre Practice, specialising in Production Sound. After university, there honestly didn't seem to be much in the way of training opportunities. I attended a course run by Orbital Sound, and I got my ABTT Bronze award. I had also attended a pyro course but most learning was on the job and no certification for it. I worked freelance for a few years on a broad mix of theatre, corporate events and school support. This included freelance work here and when a new tech role became available, I applied and got the job. The sound technician at the time left after a few months and I stepped in to cover them.

Since going full-time, training opportunities seem to be more prevalent though most have been through my employer so I now have

vocational training in things like First Aid At Work, IPAF, PASMA, and IOSH approved courses – my most recent being forklift training. I've also been able to call upon my union contacts and have courses in employment law, the environment and earlier this year got a C&G in teaching.

What steps are there on the career ladder are there for you?
Within this particular theatre there aren't many actually. From my current role, there would only be the Technical Manager's position. However, I should be able to sidestep to any of the large national houses or companies if I want to continue in theatre. Or I could move across into a production company if I wanted to do less venue specific work and stay in the industry.

What is the most challenging aspect of your job?
Dealing with limited resources – the theatre is only so big, there is only so much time in the day, there is only so much money around.

Are you freelance, or employed? What are the working hours like?
I'm employed full-time, contracted at 40 hours a week though the average working hours tend to be 50 hours per week. Our programme means that hours are concentrated near to the weekend and easier during the later week days. There is some flexibility if the show hours are less than contract and we are able to do office/maintenance work at hours that suit us.

Job Types

What is the average pay?

Pay starts at around £22,000pa for a starting full-time technician. There are payments for learning additional skills and different grades so, with overtime, the salary is around £30,000 after a year or two of employment.

What advice would you give for someone wanting to do what you do? How does someone go about getting a similar job?

Start at the bottom and work up. You may find that you actually prefer to work in a different area than you initially thought. Do find a course to study but do make sure that you do additional work outside of the course to put it into context (and make contacts and earn some money). Maths and engineering are useful things, as are additional language skills – being critically able to analyse a play is probably less useful, though every skill will come in useful at some point. Once you decide on what you want to do, make sure that everything you do is geared towards achieving that (don't get really good at pushing flightcases unless that is your ideal job) but until you decide on that, do try out a broad range of positions. Even if you decide, for example, that being part of the stage crew is not for you, knowing the basics of the role helps in your job. The entertainment industry relies on cooperation and collaboration – you can produce a show on your own but it's a lot easier with everyone working together, and a lot more fun.

What has been your favourite project to work on, and why?

The recent World Cities Residency by the Pina Bausch Tanztheatr Wuppertal was something to be part of – 10 shows across 2 venues in 6 weeks. All their shows are visually impressive (a mountaintop that pivots mid show to become a mountaincliff; a 5-ton breeze block wall that collapses at the top of the show and the show takes place on the rubble, or inside three 5 meter high earth mounds with live sheep being herded); and the company are a delight to work with.

Tom is a member of the Assocation of Sound Designers. Interview reproduced in its entirety with kind permission from the Association.

Sound No. 1, No. 2, and No.3

In long-running or large productions, the sound team are split into Sound No. 1, Sound No. 2, and Sound No. 3. Sound No. 1 is the most senior position – they are responsible for managing the sound team, budgets and scheduling. Sound No. 2 is responsible for managing sound and communication during the performance – one of their main tasks is usually managing and maintaining the radio microphones. Sound No. 3 works to assist the other members of the sound team.

Simon Sayer is a No.1 Sound. His recent projects include: Sound No.1 for We Will Rock You and supervisor on worldwide productions of We Will Rock You; also effects operator on the Olympics Opening Ceremony.

What does your job entail?
All the musicians mic's, the performers mic's, the sound effects, everything comes into the mixing desk front of house and I have to create a mix for the audience, and provide monitor mixes for the cast and musicians. Keeping a wide range of performers and musicians happy about how they sound to the audience and to each other requires a lot of diplomacy – a colleague once told me that the job is 20% making it sound good, and 80% keeping everyone happy. My job is to make the show sound as it was designed to be, to maintain that quality over the run, and to make sure everybody else does too!

What's a typical day for you?
I normally go in for 5pm, to do a sound check which is normally done by 6.15pm. Then I'll mix or supervise the show until 10.40pm when the curtain comes down. Sometimes we're needed in the daytimes for understudy and cast change reh's so

we'll come in for that. We do a lot of outside gigs – tv appearances, etc – which often involve making backing tracks and the like.

How did you get to where you are now?
I did drama at high school, then got into lighting for A Level Theatre Studies, then did the Technical Theatre course at Bristol Old Vic. After graduating I worked at Birmingham Rep for three years in the sound dept, then got a job as No.3 on Les Miserables in London, then No.2 on Blood Brothers and so on.

What's the best way to train to be a No.1?
There's lots more training courses out there now in theatre sound than when I started. After doing something like that I'd recommend getting work at a Rep house to experience a bit of everything. Coming straight into the West End and sitting on a show isn't going to give you an all round training.

What is the most challenging aspect of your job?
The mix of this show is very involved, with everyone on stage going hell for leather. We have to create the dynamics and sound of the show,

whilst keeping the composers, the MD, the actors, the producers, and of course the audience, happy. For a show like this, where the music is one of the principal attractions, it's paramount that the sound be first rate. It's quite a responsibility but not one that is often recognised.

Are you freelance, or employed?
I'm a limited company and I work on a freelance basis because I go and work on a lot of other projects. A lot of people work on a contract, increasingly on a "buy out" basis, which is where you get a set fee regardless of the hours worked. I think most No.1's get between £850 to £950 per week on a buy out. The hours are typically a 40 hour week but it varies- if we're tech'ing it can be up to 90 hours. Contracts tend to be for a year to start with, then open ended as the show runs, with the usual two weeks notice period if the show closes.

What has been your favourite project to work on, and why?

Recently it was working on the Opening Ceremony of the Olympics which was an amazing experience. We also put We Will Rock You into Las Vegas, so I was out there for 9 weeks. I produced the German and Spanish cast albums which were great fun. I really enjoy the variety.

What advice would you give for someone wanting to become a No.1?
Once you've done some training outside the West End, do everything you can to try and get a No.3 job. Be nice to everyone, get on with everybody and as soon as you can try and get on the desk and do some rehearsals. Once you've done that, the hardest leap is to go from being a No.3 to a No.2, to get the opportunity to prove that you're good enough to start mixing the show and take on that extra responsibility.

Simon is a member of the Assocation of Sound Designers. Interview reproduced in its entirety with kind permission from the Association.

Zoe Milton is a Radio Mic Technician. Her recent projects include Glyndebourne Opera Festival and the NT Live broadcast of The Curious Incident of the Dog in the Night-Time.

What does your job entail?
There are two phases – getting the show on and running the show. Getting the show on is the hard part and will often involve installing and

programming the radio mic system and liaising with Wardrobe, Wigs and Design to integrate the microphones, transmitters, in-ear-monitors into the show. I'll often start at 10 or 11am each day and work until 10 or 11pm. Running the show is a process of recreating what you set up consistently each night. Radio mics need a lot of maintenance. I'll start at 5pm on a show day.

How did you get to where you are now?

I started off doing concerts on Sundays and working in Am Dram. I went to Uni in London and applied for a Dep' job on Blood Brothers. From there I got work on other West End shows.

What's the best way to train to be a Radio Mic Technician?

The main skills you need for my job are people skills. You need to understand other people's processes – actors, SM, etc – so you can work most effectively with them. A technical/SM course is ideal for this – I've seen a lot of good people coming out of Guildhall. My Uni couldn't afford radio mics or digital desks so I didn't have any training in these when I left, but I learnt about them on the job.

What is the most challenging aspect of your job?

I'm the face of the sound department onstage – when we're putting a show on, people can get very stressed, and it can be difficult to explain to performers why they need to wear a radio mic and why we can't necessarily give them the foldback they want.

Are you freelance, or employed? What is the average pay?

I mostly work on a freelance basis, but a lot of the longer running shows work on a PAYE basis. I like the freedom and variety of being freelance, and being able to make my own hours and choose my jobs, but I don't like having to take care of the financial side of things. A freelancer might work for between £225 and £300 per day, whereas on a West End show a dep might get £65 per show and a No.3 would start off with £80 per show.

What advice would you give for someone wanting to become a Radio Mic Technician?

Be cheerful. Be chatty. Part of your job is to head trouble off before it escalates into an issue – so you need to find out how people are feeling about things. The best way to get work is to send your CV to No.1s in the West End – find out their name first. You can also get work via hire companies who are often asked to provide staff for shows.

What other roles do you do apart from sound op?

I mix shows too. I also do a lot of events for broadcast – theatre, opera, rock and roll. This varies from NT Live to Take That.

Zoe is a member of the Assocation of Sound Designers. Interview reproduced in its entirety with kind permission from the Association.

Job Types

Composer

Composers write music for performances, ranging from songs for musicals to background music for plays. Composers work with the Director and Musical Director and must be musically flexible to be able to write in a style and mood appropriate to the performance and the Director's ideas. Composers must be able to turn an idea or mood into music.

Stage Jobs Pro member Ben Osborn is a Composer.

What is the most rewarding aspect of working as a Composer?
Getting to work with incredible musicians, directors, designers, actors, and artists, as part of an ensemble.

What are the key skills required to be an effective Composer?
The ability to turn a concept into a piece of music: the main thing you need to do is to have no ego (that is, no sense that the music is 'yours'; you need to understand its purpose instead, and be objective about whether it works). You need to be open-minded to every sound and contribution, and to be very hard-working even when you don't feel inspired, as there are a lot of deadlines to be aware of.

Do you see your role as a natural step on a career ladder, and if so what is the next rung?
I'm still trying to find a way to make it cost-effective; I think that is the next step.

Please describe what a typical day working as a Composer might contain?
Going through an ever-growing list of ideas. Conversing with the director, and listening to the kind of music

that's inspiring them. Reading carefully through a script and listening to the tunes that start happening in your head, then going to a piano to play them. Recording them, trying them out on different instruments, arranging them for an ensemble. It differs, but there's a lot to do.

How did you work your way into your current role?
Student theatre gave me lots of opportunities to compose.

How much do you think networking helps towards landing a job?
A great deal.

Do you think you will be working in the industry in the next five years, and if so in what capacity?
Hopefully as a composer, writer, and songwriter.

Have you done any additional training to further your career?
No.

How important is working for free at the beginning of your career?
I'm at the beginning of my career now, and I'm working about half-and-half free/paid. If I didn't work for free, I wouldn't get a lot of work. I'm getting a day job, and I imagine I'll need to have one for a while yet.

Musical Director

The Musical Director leads the cast and musicians in the musical aspects of a performance, working with the cast to learn and perfect the music, and directing them in their vocal performance.

Stage Jobs Pro member Gareth Weedon is currently the Associate MD on Spamalot in the West End. We asked him the following questions about his career:

What is the most rewarding aspect of working as a Musical Director?
I've been lucky enough to say that I have worked with some incredibly talented singers and musicians. Couple that with working alongside musical supervisors, sound designers and directors who share your vision and aim and you have the reward. Being able to then share that each day with your audience is the ultimate satisfaction.

What are the key skills required to be an effective Musical Director?
Primarily to facilitate the intricacies of the musical score each day, consistently. To keep the show fresh for the audience: making it consistent for the supervising management; and exciting and fulfilling for all performers. As a manager yourself, being able to enthuse, encourage and empower the people on stage and in the pit to perform to their best.

Do you see your role as a natural step on a career ladder, and if so what is the next rung?
Frequently, working musical directors (and usually those who are

experienced in man-management as much as musicianship) progress to working as musical supervisors if they wish to "progress from MDing". The role is similar in nature but usually more creative in the initial stages, then consultative and more hands-off once production is running.

How did you work your way into your current role?
In my youth, I worked as a rehearsal pianist for local and regional productions. From there I went on to MD some regional pantomimes before embarking on my first national tour as assistant musical director then moving up.

How much do you think networking helps towards landing a job in the industry?
Being consistently good at what you do is what helps you move on. Being seen and heard to be doing so is what ultimately helps gain work amongst industry professionals; word of mouth plays an important part. If that means "networking" then yes, but empty networking or cold-calling rarely has any lasting effect.

Do you think you will be working in the industry in the next five years, and if so in what capacity?
I would hope to still be working in

37

five years. Ideally as a creative musical supervisor yet conducting a musical that excites me. I would also like to have written some arrangements for a show and be able to hear them regularly performed.

Please describe what a typical day working as a Musical Director might contain?

The day on an established, up-and-running show would normally begin with collating any notes from the previous evening's performance, to give to the cast. These would be given after the vocal warm up which is normally the first call of the day (assuming there are no rehearsals, auditions, or other business to attend to, that is).

Have you done any additional training courses to further your career?

Conducting lessons, observing other MDs, listening to other arrangers' work, concert-going and recording your own work are all ways to train yourself further for the role.

How important is working for free at the beginning of your career?

I think it depends from person to person. Getting your foot on the ladder involves a different route for everyone. Working for free is often a way to gain superb experience; that can either be at the beginning of or many years into one's career. You never know who among the people you're working with now will become the next big player in the field. It's competitive and exciting working amidst talent, wherever it is.

USEFUL ORGANISATIONS

The Association of Sound Designers –
www.associationofsounddesigners.com
The Association of British Theatre Technicians – *www.abtt.org.uk*

BOOKS ON SOUND

Lighting and Sound, Neil Fraser, 1993
Sound and Music for the Theatre: The Art & Technique of Design, Deena Kaye, James Lebrecht, 2009
Theatre Sound, John A. Leonard, 2001
The Stage Guide to working in lighting and sound, Geoffrey Joyce, 2008

SOUND COURSES IN THE UK

BA (Hons) Theatre Sound – Centre School of Speech & Drama
www.qurl.com/cssdtpts
BA (Hons) Performance Sound – Rose Bruford College
www.qurl.com/rosesound
BA (Hons) Sound Design For The Theatre – Royal Academy of Dramatic Art
www.qurl.com/radasound
BA (Hons) Sound Technology – Liverpool Institute of Performing Arts
www.qurl.com/lipasound
Creative Sound Technology (Foundation Degree) – De Montfort University
www.qurl.com/montfort
BA (Hons) Sound Production (Top Up) – University of Wolverhampton
www.qurl.com/wlvsound
Fd (Arts) Sound Production – University of Wolverhampton
www.qurl.com/wlvsprod
BA (Hons) Sound Design – Ravensbourne
www.qurl.com/ravesound
BSc (Hons) Sound Technology – University of Glamorgan
www.qurl.com/glamsound
Sound & Lighting for Beginners – Activate
www.qurl.com/activsl
Advanced Sound & Lighting – Activate
www.qurl.com/activtt

Technical Theatre

Theatre Technician

The Theatre Technician is responsible for setting up and preparing sound and light equipment, focusing lights, running technical rehearsals, operating the technical aspects of the production, and then de-rigging. Theatre Technicians often move on to become Technical Managers.

Stage Jobs Pro member Marita Schroeter is a Technician. We asked her the following questions about her career:

What is the most rewarding aspect of working as a Technician?
For me it is being part of something magical. There is always something undefinable and beautiful that happens when an audience watches a show, something that does not happen in rehearsals, and it stuns everyone watching it. I am proud to say I am part of the reason that this happens.

What are the key skills required to be an effective Technician?
Enthusiasm for the discipline. You have to love what you are doing and you have to want it to be as perfect as it can possibly be. Knowledge about physics you can learn if you don't have it yet, love for the thing you have to feel.

Do you see your role as a natural step on a career ladder, and if so what is the next rung?
Definitely. I am the one and only tech in my little studio venue at the moment. If I master this on my own successfully enough, I can aim higher soon I hope ...

How did you work your way into your current role?
I have been head technician in a similar sized venue before, however, the Operations Manager there was a very experienced technician as well and he made it into his mission to turn me into the best tech he could make out of me. The job I've got now I got as the technical manager of this theatre left. The Council who runs it did want to review the post before re-staffing it permanently, so she had a look on Stage Jobs Pro, found my profile, and asked me if I would be interested in covering the venue in between!

How much do you think networking helps towards landing a job in the industry?
A LOT!!!!!

Do you think you will be working in the industry in the next five years, and if so in what capacity?

I hope so, I hope I can stay a technician and by then I hope I have tried all aspects and crazy things that sometimes go with this job.

Please describe what a typical day working as a Technician might contain?

In my venue: pre-rig, welcome the company, fit up, focus lights, plot and program board, check sound effects, tech run if possible.

Have you done any additional training courses to further your career?

Yes and no. To be honest, I did the training because I did not have any work at the time, and BECTU had a lot of very cheap courses on offer. It kept me in theatres, helped my skill level and I could network during those courses.

How important is working for free at the beginning of your career?

To me it made all the difference. A head flyman saw me working on an am dram show and knew I would not get a chance at the place where I lived then. He later moved back to his hometown, and when I came to visit him he introduced me to the tech manager and senior tech in the theatre there, and made a point in telling them how good he thought I was. Those people trusted his word and gave me my first paid job ... This was almost seven years ago, and I have not looked back since

Simon Lovelace – Crew Class Q&A

WITH A CAREER SPANNING OVER 20 YEARS IN LIVE SHOWBUSINESS, SIMON LOVELACE IS ONE OF THE MOST KNOWLEDGABLE AND EXPERIENCED ALL-ROUND CREWMEN WORKING IN THE UK TODAY. HE IS ALSO AN EXCELLENT COMMUNICATOR. IN HIS ONE DAY COURSE, ENTITLED "CREW CLASS", HE IMPARTS ALL THE BASIC KNOWLEDGE REQUIRED TO TRANSFORM AN ABSOLUTE BEGINNER WITH NOTHING TO OFFER BUT INTEREST AND PASSION INTO AN EMPLOYABLE ENTRY-LEVEL STAGEHAND. SIMON WROTE THIS GUIDE TO CREWING:

I encourage all Crew Class attendees to keep in touch after attending a Crew Class day, and am frequently contacted for advice or with queries by young people making a start in the crewing industry. Some of them are considering working for one of the local crewing agencies, some are working as casuals at their local theatres. On one occasion I was asked by a degree student to contribute to his final dissertation. Here are some of the questions I've been asked over the past year, and my responses to them. I hope they will be of use to young people making career decisions in and around technical showbusiness. For more information contact **trainme@crewclass.co.uk**.

"The local crewing experience is undoubtedly the best way to get exposure to current working practices and equipment"

How significant do you believe crew work is in providing the knowledge and skills required to progress into more technical roles, such as rigger, sound engineer, backline tech etc; or managerial roles, such as stage and/or tour manager, for example?

Being a vocational trainer, maybe I'm biased. However, I'm prepared to state categorically, and challenge anyone who disagrees to prove their argument, the following. The local crewing experience is undoubtedly the best way to get exposure to current working practices and equipment in use across all areas of the modern event & theatre industry. This includes the stage and production management roles. An intelligent stage hand, who keeps their eyes and ears open and pays attention to all the areas of work activity going on around them, not just their own tasks, will very quickly build up an holistic knowledge of the entire production process. They will very quickly discover whether this kind of work is "for them" (the long hours, the physicality, the endless hanging-around), and also get firsthand exposure to specific areas of specialism they may decide to move into as their career progresses. By and large, established technicians have a positive attitude to new blood in the industry. If a newbie stagehand is seconded to, for example, the sound department to assist, and asks intelligent questions and clearly understands the answers, usually they will be more than happy to share knowledge, skills, and advice. Similarly, if the production install is going well, there will be plenty of time to talk to the crewbosses, production & stage managers etc over lunch or coffee. And again, these people will usually be very happy to share war-stories, pass on advice, and answer intelligent questions. In fact, I dare say they actually enjoy it!

What is your opinion of the wide and diverse range of training on offer both privately and in Further Education in the area of Technical Showbusiness?

There are some excellent private courses available in specialist areas. Many light and sound console manufacturers provide free training on their products, for example. There are plenty of one day pay-to-attend courses run by specialists in areas such as rigging and pyrotechnics that are of a high caliber indeed. For a more general overview there is my own one day event Crew Class (www.crewclass.co.uk), and I know of at least one Foundation Degree available that covers all the aspects of event production. However, one has to be careful before committing to colleges and universities offering Production Arts training, as the standard varies wildly. One does not need a formal BTEC or degree qualification in order to make a start in our industry. If, due to family pressure or personal choice, one chooses to commit to a higher or further education program, then "buyer, beware"! Check out the facilities on offer in the establishment. Ensure that they are up to date with the professional environment. Even more importantly, check out the tutors. A university or college interview is a two way process, don't forget. Don't be afraid to ask about the background of the teachers on the course. What is, and how recent was, their "realworld" experience?

I have been told that volunteering at my local venue and with my local amateur societies will be an excellent start to my career and improve my CV. What are your thoughts?

As a career strategy, I have to advise against it, and here are the reasons why. First and foremost, for every volunteer there are in fact two people going unpaid, when you think about it. Firstly the professional technician who hasn't been given the job because they've got a volunteer in, and secondly, the volunteer! Not only that, but if the said volunteer is paying his own bus fares and buying his own lunch, not only is he providing his time and skills for no fee, he is actually spending his own money in order to be involved! When you consider that an audience must be buying tickets, so somebody somewhere is getting money, it quickly becomes evident that this won't do. Also, promoters and producers aren't daft. If they realize that, for example, "good old Callum" will come in and operate flys for nothing, then the next time they put together a production budget they won't include the cost of a flyman – which is £100 per day or thereabouts. It sets a bad precedent. It's not good for the industry. The compromise I suggest, and put into practice when giving my own students work experience, is to strike an agreement right at the beginning. Agree daily expenses, or travel costs or a guaranteed lift. Make it perfectly clear to all that, at the end of the run, you will be expecting a thank you card with a fifty pound note in it!

Would you agree that it is possible to earn a reasonable income through event crew work, considering factors such as contract durations, working hours and pay rate etc?
Casual and agency event crew are not usually very well paid. A gross wage of in the region of £10 per hour for basic unskilled crew is the norm. However, this can be improved on by the crewperson broadening their skills base by taking on further training and getting licences in the operation of forklifts and MEWPS. Crewing companies actively encourage this personal development. Having said that, entry level crew tend to be younger people, certainly usually under the age of 30. Therefore their financial needs are much simpler than those of say, the head of a young family with mortgage commitments etc. If one is living in a shared house, or still "at home", a 40 hr week for circa £400 is an acceptable income. And a popular, competent, entry level crewperson can reasonably expect to be working an average of 40 hrs per week. A true "A-lister" will have the option to work far more, but that leads us to the dilemma raised in the next question...

How much of an impact does the physically demanding aspect of the job, have on your ability to undertake enough work to earn reasonable income?
Crew work can be physically demanding, packing and unpacking trucks, building constructions out of steeldeck and scaffolding, carrying heavy copper cable etc. But it isn't always like that. Setting up backline on stages, plugging in microphones, hanging lanterns etc can hardly be described as arduous. In fact, it could be argued that the typical crewperson's day begins and ends with a flurry of heavy physical activity, but the majority of the time is spent tweaking and twonking and hanging around! Stamina is required, but not necessarily muscular stamina. An in-demand, popular crew member will find themself doing the get-in, the stay-on (spotlight or

backline changeover) and the get-out. This adds up to a long day – 14 hrs or more is quite normal. During a busy period, they can find themself doing these kinds of day consecutively until they, literally, can do no more. Great for the bank balance, lousy for sleep patterns. So I don't think it's the physical nature of the job that's the killer, it's the hours onsite – even hanging round smoking and drinking tea for hours at a stretch – that catch up with you!

How important is it that a live event/ theatre industry professional can carry out a variety of different roles, within the industry; in order to gain enough work to earn a reasonable living?
In the early stages, absolutely vital. It's common sense that the broader your skills base, the wider the scope of work assignments you can take on. I for example, am perfectly competent in lighting and stage management, but as far as sound goes, I have no training or experience on digital desks. Therefore sound jobs requiring this skillset are a no-go area for me. And that means paid work assignments that I'm missing out on! Similarly, as one progresses from casual or local crewperson to bona fide technician, it is most likely that one's first job will be on a small touring show, and one's job description will be "technician". Obviously, this implies that one will be expected to do (and know) a bit of everything! There are seasoned technicians out there who just do monitors, or just do FOH, even some who just operate lighting boards (we call them white-glovers). But be under no illusion, these people all started off as all round crew, and were talented enough and – very important – well-liked enough to be allowed to specialize.

How important do you believe living in London, or other major cities, is, in sourcing and undertaking a substantial amount of work in the theatre & events industry; as opposed to living elsewhere and commuting to several, various locations nationally?
Sure, it helps. When I started with Stage Miracles, I was part of a "posse" that drove up to London from Hitchin. (approx 45 mins from the Wembley Complex). We were a good team, well liked, and we got all the big jobs at Wembley. However, Stage Miracles also

"It's common sense that the broader your skills base, the wider the scope of work assignments you can take on"

had plenty of little jobs going on in venues across London (eg 2 people on a 5 hr call to shift, for example, some scenery from one side of a warehouse to the other. They get paid for 5 hours, but the job actually only takes an hour and a half). We didn't get those calls, and arguably lost money as a result. Fortunately we had so much on at Wembley (and of course these were full in-show-out days) that it didn't bother us too much. As one's career progresses, however, it becomes irrelevant as to where one actually lives, as all one's work is done on location. The ideal trick is to have a high income and low living expenses. There are a considerable number of touring technicians who live in North Wales, for instance. They make their big money on tours, then return home to idyllic cottages and small holdings in the Welsh Mountains that actually cost them very little!

Is the backstage industry male dominated?
There's no easy way to put this... In my experience, of any local crew team about one in twelve to fifteen will be a girl. And, in the early stages, they are treated as "honorary blokes". So the short answer is "yes, I'm afraid so". However, I know several girls who started at the same time as me and have reached positions of respect and responsibility, particularly in the area of sound engineering. So I have to say that being female is no barrier to getting on in the industry, but in the early years you will be outnumbered. Grin and bear it: being picked on due to sex, race, or sexuality is not tolerated at any level in our industry. That is something of which we can be proud.

Crew Class is a one day pay-to-attend training course in stagecraft. Supported by the biggest companies in crewing and production, this course not only provides training, but a genuine potential leg-up into the industry. For more information go to **www.crewclass.co.uk** or email **trainme@crewclass.co.uk**.

Technical Manager/Chief Technician

The Technical Manager is in charge of the technical elements of a production, and is responsible for safety, budgeting, and discussing all the technical aspects with other members of the crew. Technical Managers usually start as Technicians and then progress to the position of Production Manager.

Stage Jobs Pro member Sebastian Barnes is a Technical Manager. We asked him the following questions about his career:

What is the most rewarding aspect of working as a Technical Manager?
Making it happen effectively, and within budget. Encouraging staff to make the most of, and develop, their skills.

What are the key skills required to be an effective Technical Manager?
Self initiative, excellent communication skills, empathy, self discipline, diplomacy, effective time and task management, effective people management, current practical theatre skills.

Do you see your role as a natural step on a career ladder, and if so what is the next rung?
Yes, Technical Manager is one natural step on a career ladder. For me the next rung could be Production Manager.

How did you work your way into your current role?
I worked to Technical Manager from casual stage technician, through a variety of technical roles, in several departments. This gave me the wide perspective necessary for a Technical Manager role.

How much do you think networking helps towards landing a job in the industry?
Networking is vital to getting into this industry. I don't agree that this should be the case. It leads to much exclusion by not being in the 'right place and the right time'.

Do you think you will be working in the industry in the next five years, and if so in what capacity?
I intend to remain working in the industry for more than five more years. I expect to develop consultancy and training roles.

Please describe what a typical day working as a Technical Manager might contain?
Phone calls and meetings arranging supplies, people and schedules for upcoming productions. Regular administrative tasks, including budgets, authorising invoices, processing orders and staff time.

Have you done any additional training courses to further your career?
Yes, A1 Skills Assessor training, various management short courses, budgeting, staff appraisal, NVQ Level 4 in Operational Management.

How important is working for free at the beginning of your career?
Working for free is only important if done in an amateur company setting, to improve your experience. Working for free for a professional company is usually damaging to your career and the employer, as it creates an unhealthy, and illegal reliance on unpaid labour.

Automation No.1 and No.2

Automation is the use of non-manually (usually electrically) powered machinery to move stage components. Automation No. 1 is the Head of Automation, and is responsible for running the automation department – organising the operation of machinery and maintaining it. Automation No.2 is the Deputy Head of Automation and assists the No.1.

Stage Jobs Pro member Nick Page is Head of Automation at Mamma Mia. We asked him the following questions about his career:

What is the most rewarding aspect of working as a Head of Automation?
For each performance we want every moving piece to work smoothly and reliably. Being able to make that happen is very rewarding. Knowing that we've worked hard to keep the cast and crew safe and so that the audience experiences the show as intended we can be sure that we have a job well done.

What are the key skills required to be an effective Head of Automation?

Automation, as a field, covers quite a wide variety of skills. When you're responsible for the whole lot, as a Head of Department, it's important that you know your system intimately, and how any one single element can affect everything else, not just within your own equipment but the whole working environment. Above all though, I think some of the most useful skills are being able to keep a calm head and always be prepared. You've also got to genuinely care about what you're doing and why you're doing it.

Do you see your role as a natural step on a career ladder, and if so what is the next rung?
I think once you reach any Head of

Department role within the theatre environment, the chances are that your next move will bring you to an altogether different discipline. As you climb that career ladder you'll inevitably find yourself in a less hands on physical role and in a progressively more managerial position. So what's next for a Head of Automation? Perhaps the skills you learn in Automation can set you up for production management, or maybe in to something more to do with engineering. Whatever it may be it's likely to be a big step in a different direction.

How did you work your way into your current role?
Good timing! Good knowledge! Lots of experience! I've been involved in technical theatre, one way or another, since I was about eight years old. Over the years I've always been keen on gaining knowledge of as many aspects of the environment as possible. Sadly though being a jack of all trades ultimately restricts your career progression so I eventually decided I needed to fix myself on a single discipline. I initially though I wanted to move in to Special Effects (Pyro and the like) but the environment I was in at the time opened my eyes to the prospects of Automation (an area of Technical Theatre I knew nothing about). The timing was perfect – here I was wanting something new to learn and position opened up to allow me to do so. And it turned out that Automation is pretty close to being a jack of all trades type of job. When I moved to London in 2007 I

once again found that timing was in my favour, but this time I also had the knowledge to back me up. So much so in fact that even as a Number 2 and a newbie to the West End, I was asked to program a brand new show. Being able to prove myself at that point is, I think, what set me up to rather rapidly make my way into an HoD role.

How much do you think networking helps towards landing a job in the industry?
I've never been a big networker as such. It would definitely be more useful if I worked more freelance jobs, but up to now I've always followed a path of full time employment and long term contracts.

Do you think you will be working in the industry in the next five years, and if so in what capacity?
Absolutely! Whether I'll still be in the West End, or even as a Head of Automation I don't know for sure. But I certainly can't see myself leaving the industry... ever.

Please describe what a typical day working as a Head of Automation might contain?
So long as everything is in good working order my normal show day can be quite simple. The department comes in to work around two and a half hours prior to show time so that we can carry our Automation Checks. This is where we move every single axis (a controllable moving piece) through their entire range of movement. This ensures

49

mechanical integrity and reliable control over the piece. Depending on the show we may also be required to help out other departments for their checks by moving set in to required positions. Once all technical checks, for all departments, are complete, the Stage is usually left in such a way so that the Cast can use it for their vocal and physical warmups. Once the cast is finished, usually just before the Half Hour Call, we preset everything to the positions they need to be in for the top of the show. At this point the Show Cloth can be dropped in and usually the House will be opened. The show itself will require at least one Operator and depending on how a show is set up other members of the department will have cues to carry out on stage, such as observing moves, checking fixings, setting pieces and so on. It's also useful to have someone available to respond to any issues that may occur during a performance, so it's advisable not to tie your department up in too many tasks. All of these tasks tend to be interchangeable within the department. So as the HoD I'm not just operating at the Control Desk. At the end of the performance we make safe, switch off and go home. We also have a day every week that is specifically set aside for Automation maintenance.

On these days we take the opportunity to inspect every element in our system, from the mechanics to the electronics, and if we find anything out of place we make good. We also carry out a preventative maintenance schedule, which aims to prevent the eventuality of discovering major issues.

Have you done any additional training courses to further your career?

There are plenty of opportunities to further my knowledge through training. I've certainly considered several courses, but to be honest my main training has been through real life experience. There are, however, certain things I know I will eventually specifically want to learn, depending on where I take my career over the years.

How important is working for free at the beginning of your career?

This is a difficult question. Generally I would say you should never be taken advantage of, so don't accept work that doesn't pay. That said; the start of my career was all voluntary, and the advantage of voluntary work is that, if you're with others that volunteered, you all want to be there and you all want to learn. It can be a terribly encouraging environment.

Stage Technologies & Automation

THIS GUIDE WAS KINDLY WRITTEN BY STAGE TECHNOLOGIES

Stage Technologies was founded in 1994 as one of the world's first dedicated theatre automation specialists and became an instrumental player in bringing the extensive benefits of automation technology to the live performance industry. We employ more than 180 automation engineers, manufacturing specialists and support staff around the world.

Stage Technologies has worked closely with Cirque du Soleil® since 2003 on some of their boldest theatrical endeavours such as Iris, The Beatles LOVE™ and KA™, which are designed to confront the boundaries of both the imagination and physics. Other end users of our equipment and systems include Blue Man Group, The Royal Opera House, Royal Shakespeare Company, The Royal Conservatoire of Scotland, Disney, Dragone, the Rotterdamse Schouwberg, Brussels Opera House, Göteborgs Stadsteater, Princess Cruises, the War Memorial Opera House (San Francisco Opera), Hong Kong Cultural Centre, Sydney Theatre and Perth Performing Arts Centre and many more.

There are several different career paths in stage automation:

• Engineers design the control, mechanical and software products used to power the movement of props, performers and large scale set pieces such as revolves.

• Workshop technicians assemble, test and ship the equipment all around the world.

• The after sales support team available to help clients; this availability is crucial as more and more venues are installing automation systems. A good support team is able to recommend solutions even for equipment produced by a competing company.

• Automation operators are seated backstage at many West End shows, running through the plotted axes that move the sets and performers.

• Sales and marketing staff seek out opportunities to promote the business brand in front of potential clients such as theatre consultants, producers and architects.

51

- The best of all of these professionals combine their training and experience with a love of theatre and performance, and are therefore able to speak the language of the creative teams.

One way to learn more about automation is to read the book by our two founders Mark Ager and John Hastie, "Automation in the Entertainment Industry." The book is available in print and for Kindle.

This guide was kindly written by Stage Technologies, one of the world's first dedicated theatre automation specialists. You can find out more at **www.stagetech.com**.

USEFUL ORGANISATIONS

The Association of British Theatre Technicians – *www.abtt.org.uk*

Stage Technoloiges – *www.stagetech.com*

BOOKS ON TECHNICAL THEATRE

Technical Theatre for Nontechnical People, Drew Campbell, 2005

Technical Theatre: A Practical Introduction, Christine White, 2001

Automation in the Entertainment Industry, Mark Ager, John Hastie, 2009

TECHNICAL THEATRE COURSES IN THE UK

BA (Hons) Technical and Production Management – Central School of Speech and Drama

www.qurl.com/cssdtech

BA (Hons) Technical Effects for Performance – London College of Fashion

www.qurl.com/londonte

BA (Hons) Technical Theatre – Mountview Academy of Theatre Arts

www.qurl.com/mounttech

PG Dip Technical Theatre – Mountview Academy of Theatre Arts

www.qurl.com/mountpg

BA (Hons) Technical Theatre and Stage Management – Royal Academy of Dramatic Art

www.qurl.com/radatech

BA (Hons) Theatre Arts (Design and Technical Theatre) – Middlesex University

www.qurl.com/middletech

BA (Hons) Theatre and Screen: Technical Arts and Special Effects – Wimbledon School of Art

www.qurl.com/wimtech

BA (Hons) Technical Theatre Arts – Guildhall School of Music and Drama

www.qurl.com/gsmdtech

BA Technical and Production Arts – Royal Scottish Academy of Music and Drama

www.qurl.com/tpa

Stage Management & Technical Theatre Course (Two Year Foundation Degree) – London Academy of Music and Dramatic Art

www.qurl.com/lamdatech

TECHNICAL THEATRE COURSES IN THE UK (CONTINUED)

Stage Management & Technical Theatre Foundation Degree – ALRA (Academy of Live and Recorded Arts)
www.qurl.com/alrasmte

Fda/BA (Hons) Stage Management & Technical Theatre – East 15 Acting
School www.qurl.com/eastsmte

BA (Hons) Theatre Studies and Technical Stage Production – Staffordshire University
www.qurl.com/stafftech

Technical Theatre Skills (Foundation) – City Literary Institute
www.qurl.com/citytech

Technical Theatre Arts – BRIT School of Performing Arts
www.qurl.com/brittech

Technical Theatre (Foundation Degree) – Huddersfield University
www.qurl.com/hudtech

BA (Hons) Technical Theatre – Huddersfield University
www.qurl.com/hudtechba

BTEC Subsidiary Award Technical Theatre – Lewisham College
www.qurl.com/lewistech

Theatre arts (Technical Theatre) (Foundation Degree) – New College Nottingham
www.qurl.com/ncntech

Stage Management and Technical Theatre (Foundation Degre) – Hull College
www.qurl.com/hulltech

BA (Hons) Stage Management and Technical Theatre – Hull College
www.qurl.com/hullba

Technicians Training Day – Activate
www.qurl.com/activday

Stage Technologies run various automation courses throughout the year –
www.stagetech.com/training

CrewClass provide 1 day training sessions throughout the year –
www.crewclass.co.uk

The ABTT runs regular technical training courses for their members –
www.abtt.org.uk/courses.htm

Stage Management

Stage Manager

The role of Stage Manager is highly varied and often high pressure, as they are in charge of everything on and off stage during performances to ensure the production runs to the highest standard. Stage Managers must be excellent communicators, good at working under pressure, excel at problem solving, and be very efficient. Stage Managers often progress from being Assistant Stage Managers or Deputy Stage Managers, and can then move on to work as Company Stage Manager or Production Manager.

Assistant Stage Manager

Assistant Stage Managers are responsible for maintaining the stage, sourcing and looking after props, helping cast and crew, doing paperwork or covering for the Deputy Stage Manager during the rehearsal and production process. The most obvious career progression is to the position of Deputy Stage Manager and then Stage Manager.

Stage Jobs Pro member Beth Crock is an ASM. We asked her the following questions about her career:

What is the most rewarding aspect of working as a Assistant Stage Manager?

The most rewarding part of working as an assistant stage manager is the fact that I truly love what I do. I love the variety that comes with working freelance. No two days are ever the same and I get to meet so many different people, and learn something new every day. I enjoy the challenge of sourcing and organising props and of working with a variety of performers, technicians and creatives.

What are the key skills required to be an effective Assistant Stage Manager?

There are two main components to working as an ASM. Firstly to help source and look after any props and furniture for a production, and secondly to support the stage management team, performers, and creatives throughout the rehearsal and production process. An ASM should have a strong initiative and be motivated to work independently. If you are sent out to find a specific prop, you should know where and how to look for it without constantly having to consult the stage manager or designer. The ability to think on your feet is very important. Productions and situations are constantly changing, so it is good to be able to adapt and come up with solutions to problems as they arise. It is also vital to have excellent inter-

personal skills and to be able to work with and communicate effectively with everyone involved in the production. A willingness to be flexible is also essential. There are sometimes unpleasant jobs that must be done that often fall to the ASM to complete. Someone has to do them, so you might as well do it well and do it cheerfully. There are also some really fun elements so you need to be able to take the good with the bad.

Do you see your role as a natural step on a career ladder, and if so what is the next rung?

Personally, I prefer the role of ASM above any other position. For myself, I do not see it as a stepping stone to becoming a DSM or stage manager, but it is an excellent starting place for others considering a career in stage management. I am perfectly capable of working in these roles, and I have done so in the past, yet I still prefer working as an ASM. The next step up the career ladder for me would be to find a permanent position in a regional repertory producing house.

How did you work your way into your current role?

I did a three year BA (Hons) course in Stage Management and Technical Theatre, and I feel it was an excellent preparation for working in the professional theatre world. Part of the training was to get me out and working with professionals. My first proper job came as a direct result of the secondment I competled as part of my degree. Since then, I have been working freelance with very few breaks in employment. I have worked on a variety of productions, including a pantomime that was advertised on Stage Jobs Pro. Nearly every company I have worked for has asked me back to work with them again. All work leads to more work, so it is important to leave a positive impression.

How much do you think networking helps towards landing a job in the industry?
Networking can be very important to getting work in the industry. Several of my jobs have come as a direct result of being put forward by someone I know. In other jobs I have found that I quite often have worked with the same people or for the same companies as the new people I meet. I like to think I have a good working reputation with colleagues and that if I am mentioned, they will speak positively of me, just as I do with people I think highly of myself.

Do you think you will be working in the industry in the next five years, and if so in what capacity?
I very much hope to be working in the industry in five years' time. I would like to still be working as an ASM but working for larger companies more consistently and making a bit more money.

Please describe what a typical day working as a Assistant Stage Manager might contain?
No two days working as an ASM will every be the same, but they can be lumped into several categories:

propping, assisting in rehearsals and onstage. A day propping can be spent tromping around trying to find props and furniture for a show. Depending on the design and budget, I will visit a variety of different shops and potentially hire houses. In London I have several "propping routes" which include areas with a concentration of useful shops, charity, junk, second-hand, discount stores, Army/Navy surplus, etc. A propping day can also be spent researching, looking at a specific period or style for a prop. The internet is also an extremely useful resource for finding objects farther afield such as Ebay or Gumtree, or specialist online shops. Generally most of my days during the rehearsal period will be propping days. Sometimes the DSM will need someone to assist in rehearsals. If the DSM is not there at all, the ASM can cover the book, writing in blocking, prompting and taking notes as a direct cover for the DSM. Quite often if there is a large cast or a complicated props plot, it is very useful as an ASM to be in the rehearsal room setting and running prop and assisting the performers. This can be really useful to get an idea of how the show will run once it moves into the theatre. Onstage the ASM will ensure that all props and furniture are set correctly and will quite often sweep and mop the stage as necessary. During the technical period, the ASM needs to be on hand all the time to help wherever necessary: scene changes, handing props, paging doors, herding performers. This is where they will develop a running plot to use during performances. During showcall the ASM will help to prepare the stage and props for the show and then run any cues they have during the performance and then do any cleaning up afterwards.

Have you done any additional training courses to further your career?

I trained for my career at the Guildhall School of Music and Drama. My training included courses in health and safety, risk assessment, use of access equipment, manual handling, first aid as well as basic instruction in all areas of backstage. I particularly chose to focus on stage management as well as design realisation and electrics. I feel this was very important in starting my career and providing a good foundation from which to work. Personally I have not done any further training courses, but am considering doing so in order to keep up with changes in the industry due to legislation and advances in technology.

How important is working for free at the beginning of your career?

I very strongly believe that it is wholly UNACCEPTABLE to work for free at the beginning of my career. I spent three years training in a professional environment and was fully able to take on a properly paid position from the day I finished my course. I made the mistake of doing several shows in the London Fringe for very little money, and I now have a reputation within certain circles for being willing to work for nothing. This is NOT an image I want to promote as this is my career, not a hobby. I have to make a living, and there are plenty of companies out there that have been and are willing to pay me a living wage at the beginning of my career. Working for free in stage management encourages low production values and I believe can damage the theatre industry as a whole. More of us need to stand up and insist to be paid a living wage for a job well done. However, working for free as a PART of training can be a very useful experience, but only if you are working alongside a full team of professionals, rather than acting in a role of full responsibility. I had a very useful work experience placement in which I effectively worked as an extra ASM in addition to a full stage management team. I learned so much from the people I was working with and they treated me as another member of the team. There was no pressure on me to deliver as the only ASM, which allowed me to put my full effort into learning as much as I could. The company I worked for was so satisfied with my work experience that the following season they asked me back as a full professional. There is a time and place for working for free, but it should not be part of the professional period of anyone's career.

Deputy Stage Manager / Showcaller

During the rehearsal Deputy Stage Managers compile notes on prompts, cues and blocking. During a performance they 'call the show', i.e., they give the orders with regard to sound and lighting cues or actors' entrances. Deputy Stage Managers have often moved up from being an Assistant Stage Manager, and often progress to the position of Stage Manager.

© RICHARD CAMPBELL

Stage Jobs Pro member Carol Pestridge is a DSM. We asked her the following questions about her career:

What is the most rewarding aspect of working as a Deputy Stage Manager?
Getting the audience reaction after the first night performance. Seeing all of the hard work pay off.

What are the key skills required to be an effective Deputy Stage Manager?
Good communication and people skills, diplomacy, enthusiasm, stamina, a cool head and the ability to multi task.

Do you see your role as a natural step on a career ladder, and if so what is the next rung?
Yes. I have already taken work as a Stage Manager and I would love to do Company Stage Managing in the future.

How did you work your way into your current role?
After finishing my degree in film and theatre studies I did voluntary ASM work and took a few jobs as a Wardrobe Mistress. Once I had this on my CV I got paid work as an ASM and eventually worked my way up to DSM by doing book cover. After my first DSM job I have pretty much got every job from recommendations and word of mouth.

How much do you think networking helps towards landing a job in the industry?
It certainly helps if people know you, as they can recommend you to others if they are in need of a stage manager.

Do you think you will be working in the industry in the next five years, and if so in what capacity?
Yes. Probably still in a form of Stage Management.

Please describe what a typical day working as a Deputy Stage Manager might contain?
Get up and go to the rehearsal space. Grab milk on the way in. Clean the space and put the kettle

on. Have a cup of tea. Once the director and actors are in I take notes during rehearsal, prompt and add any cues or blocking to the book. At the end of the rehearsal I go through the schedule with the director. Once I have locked up the rehearsal room I call the ASM on the way home to give any updates. Once I get home I send out the schedule for the next day. Type up and email out the rehearsal notes. Have dinner then crawl into bed.

Have you done any additional training courses to further your career?
No. Well I have done fire warden and health and safety training but I don't think it has furthered my career.

How important is working for free at the beginning of your career?
Well if you can get paid work straight away then great! But it is a very good way of gaining experience and adding to your CV. Yes, I think that it is important.

Technical Stage Manager
On smaller and touring productions a Technical Stage Manager is often employed who combines the roles of Technician and Stage Manager.

Company Stage Manager
Company Stage Managers combine the roles of Stage Manager and Company Manager. They have a wide variety of responsibilities – supervising the get in, managing publicity opportunities for the cast, doing paperwork, managing the technical aspects of the production, and much else. Company Stage Managers may progress to working as Company Manager or Production Manager, and may previously have worked as Assistant Stage Manager, Deputy Stage Manager, and Stage Manager.

Stage Jobs Pro member Justin Savage is a CSM. We asked him the following questions about his career:

What is the most rewarding aspect of working as a Company Stage Manager?

One of the most rewarding aspects of working as a CSM is playing a large part in helping to bring a show to life every night; a well managed company is a happy company, and a happy company makes for a better show. The better the show, the happier the audience.

What are the key skills required to be an effective Company Stage Manager?

Communication. The CSM is the link between the Production Office and the Acting Company, the Actors and Stage Management, the company and the theatre. It is vital to keep all of these parties well informed at all times. Show sense. If you're not getting the biggest kick out of enter- taining several hundred people every night, and you're doing it because you like fiddling about with gaffer tape, you shouldn't be doing the job. We put on shows; it's a privilege, enjoy it. Practical ability. Common sense. A calm head. Boundless energy. Diplomacy.

Do you see your role as a natural step on a career ladder, and if so what is the next rung?

The job is enormously satisfying in its own right. However it is also a very useful stepping stone to, amongst other things, producing, general management, casting and production management. As CSM, one gets to see far more of the 'big picture' than more specialised roles within our industry.

How did you work your way into your current role?

I began as an ASM with a tiny dance company. I then worked my way through every aspect of Stage Management, and ran my own production company for several years. However, as a job, CSM was always the position from which I derived the most satisfaction. This is a role to which I have returned, and very happily too.

How much do you think networking helps towards landing a job in the industry?

Networking is vital. This is a big industry, but not so big that one can get lost; the more one stays in touch the better the odds of hearing about that next plum job.

Do you think you will be working in the industry in the next five years, and if so in what capacity?

Yes, I intend to continue in the industry for the next five years at least, either as CSM or in some other role, as yet undefined. You never know what's round the next corner.

Please describe what a typical day working as a Company Stage Manager might contain?

If I'm running a get-in, I'll be at the theatre at 07.30. I then supervise the load-in and fit up. On even the smallest touring show this will consume all of that working day, to be ready to open that night. Once in, and up, and running smoothly, a typical touring day might consist of checking with Marketing and Publicity to see if the cast have any radio or TV interviews, working out next week's payroll, scheduling paint and maintenance calls, booking a doctor's appointment for a company member, discussing strategy with the producer and/or the theatre and then preparing to do the same thing all over again at next week's venue. The welfare of the company is paramount, and a conscientious CSM will pay this aspect of the job due diligence. Regular, informal chats with everyone in the group pays dividends in keeping things on an even keel. Theatre is full of personalities; they need to be looked after.

Have you done any additional training courses to further your career?

None whatsoever. Everything I have learned, I have learned on the job.

How important is working for free at the beginning of your career?

That's a tricky one. There's a fine line between gathering useful experience and getting exploited. We all have value; take your space, don't be shy, make sure your efforts are rewarded.

Company Manager

The Company Manager oversees the management of the production, performing day-to-day administrative tasks, such as dealing with legal and contractual work, and paying the cast and crew. Company Managers need to be good communicators, good at budgeting, and have strong problem-solving skills.

Stage Management as a Career

THIS IS AN ABRIDGED VERSION OF THE CAREER GUIDE WRITTEN, COMPILED AND EDITED BY MEMBERS OF THE STAGE MANAGEMENT ASSOCIATION, REPRODUCED HERE WITH KIND PERMISSION. YOU CAN DOWNLOAD THE FULL GUIDE FREE OF CHARGE AT ***www.stagemanagementassociation.co.uk***
© STAGE MANAGEMENT ASSOCIATION, 2012

This is essentially a "people management" job. A Stage Manager must have the temperament and ability to get along with people in both the artistic and technical sides of theatre, and to understand what they do. It is part of the attraction of the work that each new job will introduce new and different challenges. However, the work is never glamorous, often involving long hours and fairly boring, repetitive tasks as well as being physically demanding.

During the initial rehearsal period, the stage management team is responsible for:

- Marking out the set on the floor of the rehearsal room with coloured mark-up tape, based on the designer's ground plan.
- Arranging for basic catering facilities.
- Arranging substitute or rehearsal furniture and props.
- Scheduling rehearsals, and ensuring that all artistes and creative departments are aware of these calls.
- Collecting information about the production e.g. details of sets and costumes, sound and lighting requirements, props, and prop-making and ensuring these are copied to the relevant departments.
- Making sure that the director's wishes are passed on to the appropriate departments.
- Liaising with the Production Manager on costings and production schedules.

"A Stage Manager must have the temperament and ability to get along with people in both the artistic and technical sides of theatre, and to understand what they do"

"Making sure that they and the director have the optimum conditions with the best atmosphere and least distractions in which to work is the ultimate goal"

- Supervising the gradual introduction of the actual playing furniture and props.
- Making prop and furniture setting and running lists as the production develops.
- Removing the entire remaining physical production including furniture, props and costumes – both rehearsal and playing – from the rehearsal room and into the base or first theatre.

In addition to this, the welfare of the actors is of paramount importance. Making sure that they and the director have the optimum conditions with the best atmosphere and least distractions in which to work is the ultimate goal.

When the show has opened and is running, the stage management is responsible for the management of each evening's performance. This involves setting up the stage and wings with the furniture and props required for the production; checking that all artistes are in the building by their allotted times; giving 'calls' to the actors before and during the show, and other cues to all departments, enabling the changing of scenery, lighting and sound to be co-ordinated. During the run, maintaining and replacing props as necessary.

In summary, the SM takes an overview to keep the show as the director directed and both the actors and technicians happy.

In smaller scale theatre or on tour, the stage management may also be required to 'roadie'; that is drive, load and unload trucks, put up the set, and design and/or operate both sound and lighting.

This brief description gives some idea of the variety and responsibility of the job. The acting company must trust their stage management team. In a crisis it must always be the stage management that remain cool, keep their heads and cope with it. In a confrontation situation stage management must calm, soothe and mediate.

Touring or 'One Home'

There is a radical difference between taking a show from venue to venue on tour and a West End or producing theatre show which is static, and the duties are very different for both. With the ever tightening budgets of producing managements, the total team for any but the largest touring shows are usually three – or four at the most – plus wardrobe. This means an ever-expanding multiplicity of duties, encompassing the whole spectrum of theatre, is needed to cope with the weekly move and set-up of the show. On tour, the stage management team are expected to arrive at the venue, usually on a Monday morning, put up the set (CSM), organise and set furniture and props and 'dress' the production (DSM, ASM) with the accessories specified by the designer.

The CSM often then has to rig, focus and relight the show working from plans and notes supplied by the Lighting Designer, which is time consuming and can take up most of the day.

The other stage management, working with the resident staff, are also expected to set up and specify areas for extra scenery and furniture storage if necessary, e.g. if used in another act; show cuelight and practical light positions for the resident electrics staff, arrange for the offstage areas to be cleaned and carpeted etc., and sometimes to organise and rehearse key scene and act changes with the show staff, in addition to any prop setting, sound checks and other stage management chores they may have. It can be a very busy day!

On larger scale touring productions there may be a production carpenter and sometimes also a production electrician (or either one singly) to put the set up and light the show. This relieves some of this burden from the CSM and allows the other jobs to be shared out more proportionally with the rest of the team.

On the largest shows – predominantly musicals – the stage management usually need only to focus their efforts on 'pure' stage management. It stands to reason that the stage management have to rapidly build up a strong relationship with the resident staff, especially if the show is to open the same night. This sounds daunting, but one must bear in mind that this occurs nearly every Monday in theatres around the country and the resident crew are hardened to it, as you will become. Many teams have a great rapport with the theatre crew and it becomes a social as well as a professional pleasure to work at the venue. Equally, any shortcomings usually only have to be borne for a week – or two – at the most, as another town beckons on the tour.

In the West End, the Production Manager, Designer and at least one Production Carpenter are always present on the fit up to work with the resident Master Carpenter and his staff while lighting is overseen by the Lighting Designer and his production electrician in tandem with the theatre's Chief Electrician and his staff, so most of the carpentry and electrical chores will be handled exclusively by them.

The stage management will, however, need to view the theatre as their home for at least the next few months and so prop table placement, prop and furniture storage and setting will need to be carefully thought out and permanently marked up. All technical requirements such as sound, cameras and monitors for the prompt desk, and communications equipment will be hired in specifically for the venue and so will need to be carefully positioned and tested as they won't have had the 'bedding-in' in that touring affords. There has to be much greater liaison between the theatre staff and the stage management as whatever is decided, be it equipment positions, settings or scene changes will, once set, usually be the standard for the run.

Again, as with touring, an early solid relationship with the theatre staff is helpful and even more important than on tour as you may be there for several months, if not years. While it is important to gently but firmly exhibit and impose your standards and work practices upon the staff, remember that they have been there a lot longer than you and with countless productions and may take time to adjust.

In producing theatres, the fit up would also be undertaken by the resident Master Carpenter or Technical Stage Manager and his staff, and the lighting would be rigged and focussed by the resident electrics crew under the instruction of the Lighting Designer; those and any other technical departments (automation, AV, sound, etc.) would be overseen by the Production Manager at this stage.

The stage management will probably still be busy in the rehearsal room whilst this is going on and will have one or two days at most to set up the backstage areas as required. It is at the technical rehearsal that they will assume responsibility for the show, taking over from the Production Manager.

Runs of shows in such producing theatres are often for about 3-4 weeks, but can be shorter or longer. If the show is a co-production, stage management will have to plan the handover to another team at the end of their run; but most shows will simply end after their run and stage management's duties are to dispose of or return any props and furniture and other equipment which had been borrowed or hired or made specifically for the production, unless it is to be stored for future use. Your relationship with the resident staff will already have been established during the rehearsal period as you will have been, most likely, rehearsing in or near the building where you will ultimately run the show. It is no less important for that, especially as they may know the building much better than you if you are just working freelance on one show, and can be very helpful whilst you learn to find your way around.

Then there are the local authorities to satisfy. You will need to prepare a full risk assessment on the production particularly in respect of safety in all aspects of the show. Particular attention should be taken with naked flame, smoke or mist, special effects, pyrotechnics, firearms, light fittings and even set construction. Good control methods must be in place and observed by everyone.

With unusual sets, extension to the stage into the auditorium, performer flying etc. the local council may send a representative to check all constructions from a Buildings and Safety perspective.

"*You will need to prepare a full risk assessment on the production particularly in respect of safety in all aspects of the show*"

The Production Manager will have all of these areas under his control and with the CSM will take the various agencies for a tour of the production, indicating areas that might be of interest or concern, and indicating the measures that have been taken to deal with any potential problem. S/He will also supply related paperwork for the production, such as certification for rigging sets and fire retardant timber. These will be needed not only by the authorities, but by the technical managers for the theatre.

The DSM and ASM may be needed to have on hand any special, flame or other effects that the authorities may require to be demonstrated, in order to include them on the licence.

Job Types

Career Structure

There is often, or for most people, a progression through the roles, starting as ASM, later moving into being a DSM, and later again into SM and/or CSM.

However, as the roles are quite different and require quite different skills and temperaments, most people will find a particular liking or talent for one of the roles, spending years as ASM, for example, because they enjoy propping and prop-making; or the bulk of their career as DSM because they love being in rehearsals and cueing the show; or considerable time as SM/CSM because they are good at, and like, being in charge.

For many – by no means all – stage managers there comes a time, too, when they feel they need to move on from stage management, for a variety of reasons. Often this point occurs around 10 to 15 years into their career. Within the industry, there are many roles they can move into, depending on their individual skills, interests and wishes.

Frequently, stage managers become production managers (building based or freelance) or company managers; they can also become administrators, producers or general managers; they might take up directing; or work for a supplier or manufacturer; or set up their own business, for example as prop maker or buyer. Stage managers also become lighting designers, agents, trade unionists, trainers, teachers, theatre consultants, venue managers and journalists to name just a few recent examples.

"Historically, there has always been about an equal number of men and women working in stage management"

Many at the latter end of their stage management career work extensively in conference/corporate and public events of all kinds (e.g. Queen's Golden Jubilee, Olympic opening ceremonies, large festivals etc.), but only very few are able to turn this into a full-time career as there are limited amounts of opportunities.

Some, but not many, stage managers move into television and film. Most stage managers, unless they leave the industry altogether, prefer to stick with the live arts.

Historically, there has always been about an equal number of men and women working in stage management and the ideal team is usually considered to be one in which both sexes are represented. This balance is about to be restored after recent decades saw a shift towards more women in stage management – the last five to ten years have seen an increase in the numbers of men applying and taking up courses in stage management.

What do you do now?

Go and talk to a stage manager at your nearest producing theatre or if there is a touring company visiting your area, talk to the stage manager about their job and how they gained entry into the profession.
Experience gained through school productions, youth theatre or amateur groups is invaluable. You may even be able to get casual work from time to time at your local professional theatre. In the last instance make an appointment to see the Production/Stage Manager to talk about the possibilities.

Training

Vocational training for stage management is available at many drama schools and these courses are mainly, but not exclusively, at degree level.

Selection is by interview and most courses require GCSE and A level/BTEC qualifications or previous experience in the industry. Although you may not be required to have A-levels or a BTEC (and they don't have to be in 'drama'), they are important and may help the school to decide if you will be able to undertake the study involved. Practical experience, such as with your local theatre, amateur theatre group or on school productions is highly valued by drama schools.

Funding for courses is extremely limited but you should always check with your Local Education Authority as to what is available from your council. Each individual drama school's admissions officer will also be able to give you funding information. The funding situation for degree courses is the same as for any university degree.

Some colleges, universities and drama schools have scholarships or bursaries so contact them directly as these tend to change from year to year.

If you have A-Levels or a BTEC, you may like to take a degree or diploma course in drama or drama related subjects, before going into vocational training at postgraduate level. This would give you a deeper appreciation of the history of the theatre and how it is related to its social, historical and geographical contexts, as well as giving you an introduction to the skills required for working in professional theatre. However, there is virtually no funding at postgraduate level.

While people can and do enter the profession without training, the chances of getting a job are vastly improved if you have trained on a vocational course (particularly one at a college which is a member of Drama UK).

Recently, new creative apprenticeships have been introduced by CCSkills, the sector skills council for the creative and cultural industries. Whilst they don't offer a dedicated stage management apprenticeship, it is possible to use the Technical Theatre apprenticeship as a springboard and specialise in stage management further down the road (**www.creative-choices.co.uk/knowledge/creative-apprenticeships**).

A number of theatres also offer local apprenticeship schemes and the on-the-job training can be complemented with short courses from the Association of British Theatre Technicians (ABTT) (**www.abtt.org.uk**) or the Stage Management Association (SMA) (**www.stagemanagementassociation.co.uk**) and work placements with other employers.

A career as a Stage Manager

Apart from the specific elements of work in this business, there are other practical and personal requirements. You will need to be a good self-motivator, and will need to manage most of your business affairs yourself. One-off projects and team working can provide a great sense of achievement over short periods of time. You can choose when and for whom you work. You will need to consider the effect of a peripatetic and irregular work pattern on your social and family life. Ill health can mean you cannot earn or get benefits.

Income tax: Ignorance is no defence, you need to be aware of and understand the tax categories of PAYE (Pay as you earn) or Self-Assessment/Schedule D. You can be both employed and self-employed in this business. Some employments are classed as PAYE, some freelance patterns of work can qualify for Schedule D status, but in most of their contracts stage managers, like actors, will qualify for the dual status of paying Class 1 National Insurance (like an employee, entitling you to sign on in between contracts), but paying tax like a freelance worker (entitling you to offset legitimate business expenses against tax).

Self-employment means you have to register with HMRC (Her Majesty's Revenue and Customs), keep your own records of income and expenses, make your returns by the January 31st that follows the end of each tax year (April 5th), and pay the bill in two installments as demanded. It mainly means you should not spend all the money you earn! Keep about a third aside for tax and nasty surprises and you might have a little to spare at the end of the year when you have paid your tax. Tax Officers are obliged to help – though some peace of mind can be bought in the form of advice from an accountant.

"You will need to be a good self-motivator, and will need to manage most of your business affairs yourself"

National Insurance Contributions: Class 1, or 2 and 4, depending on your tax status, can affect your eligibility for benefits. If you have been paying Class 1 NI, you are entitled to apply for jobseeker's allowance; if you pay Class 2 or 4, you cannot do this. Individual offices often do not have the correct information with regard to stage managers' dual tax status, in line with that of actors. Equity is very much involved in this area, and the best source of advice.

Personal Pension / Private Health Insurance / Unemployment Insurance: decisions made now can affect your future. How much can you afford to spend? You need to take advice from someone you can trust. Equity and BECTU have some schemes with some employers to set up pension contributions during engagements. You will probably need your own scheme as well.

Health and Safety: It is essential for all to be aware of the law, and of the personal responsibility for one's own safety and the potential to affect the safety of others. This is a dangerous industry, we use products in ways they are not normally used, we work in bad light, and there is a lot of adrenaline flowing around when we work. The Health and Safety Executive produces free and priced information on H&S issues and legislation. You should get their leaflet Facts for Freelancers in Broadcasting and the Performing Arts. The ABTT and SMA publish regular information about safe practice.

Public Liability Insurance: A grey area. This covers you against injuring a member of the public by your activities. Not legally required, but sometimes needed. Equity and BECTU offer Public Liability Insurance as part of the benefits of membership.

Getting a Job

A full driving licence is invaluable and the importance of trying to obtain one and keeping it "clean" cannot be overestimated, as the job often entails collecting props or scenery, or driving a fringe company between venues.

The ability to read a musical score enlarges one's job prospects.

Extracts from the SMA Career Guide courtesy of the Stage Management Association. The full guide can be downloaded from **www.stageman-agementassociation.co.uk/shop/free-stage-management-career-guide**, along with details of SMA memberships including student membership.

Useful Organisations
The Stage Management Association –
www.stagemanagementassociation.co.uk

Books on Stage Management
Stage Management and Theatre Administration, Pauline Menear and Terry Hawkins, 1993
Stage Management: The Essential handbook, Gail Pallin, 2010
Essential Guide to Stage Management, Scott Palmer, 2000

Basics – A Beginner's Guide to Stage Management, Peter Coleman, 2007
Backstage Guide to Stage Management: Running a Show from First Rehearsal to Last Performance, Kelly Thomas, 1999
The Stage Guide to stage management, Barbara Eifler, 2008

Stage Management courses in the UK
BA (Hons) Stage Management – Central School of Speech and Drama
www.qurl.com/cssdsm
BA (Hons) Stage Management – Rose Bruford College
www.qurl.com/rosesm

BA (Hons) Stage Management – The Royal Welsh College of Music and Drama
www.qurl.com/rwcmdsm
MA Stage Management – The Royal Welsh College of Music and Drama
www.qurl.com/rwcmdma

BA (Hons) Technical Theatre and Stage Management – Royal Academy of Dramatic Art

www.qurl.com/radattsm

FdA Professional Stage Management (Two Year) – Bristol Old Vic Theatre School

www.qurl.com/fdasm

BA (Hons) Professional Stage Management – Bristol Old Vic Theatre School
www.qurl.com/oldvicsm

BA (Hons) Stage and Costume Management – Guildhall School of Music and Drama

www.qurl.com/gsmdsm

Stage Management & Technical Theatre (Two Year Foundation degree) – London Academy of Music and Dramatic Art

www.qurl.com/lamdasm

BA (Hons) Performance Management – University of Winchester

www.qurl.com/winpm

Stage & Production Management (Foundation Degree) – Northbrook College

www.qurl.com/northsm

FdA Theatre Production (Design and Management) –
University of West London

www.qurl.com/uwlprod

FdA Stage Management and Technical Theatre – Hull College

www.qurl.com/hullsmtt

BA (Hons) Top up Stage Management and Technical Theatre – Hull College

www.qurl.com/hulltopup

BTEC Arts (Stage Management) – Hull College

www.qurl.com/hullsm

BA (Hons) Event Management – Southhampton Solent University

www.qurl.com/eventman

The Stage Management Associations runs classes throughout the year which are open to members and non-members –

www.stagemanagementassociation.co.uk/training

Costume, Make-up and Wardrobe

Costume Assistant

Costume Assistants work with the Costume Designer to help design, develop, and create costumes for the cast. Costume Assistants must have excellent sewing skills, a good understanding of design and an eye for detail. Costume Assistants naturally progress to work as Costume Designers and Costume Makers, and from there can move on to become Costume Supervisors.

Costume Designer

The Costume Designer plays a very important role in a production as they design and conceive costumes for the cast which helps to set the play in a particular period or genre and convey the intended mood of the play and roles of the characters. The Costume Designer will often work with the Director to ensure that the costumes agree with the Director's vision for the play, work with the Costume Maker on the construction of the costumes and choice of materials, and will have a Costume Assistant to help them. Costume Designers can progress to become Costume Supervisors.

Costume Maker

Costume Makers are responsible for enabling the construction of the costumes – they translate the Costume Designer's ideas and designs into real costumes. This involves numerous jobs – sourcing the materials, liaising with the Costume Designer and Costume Supervisor, creating patterns for the costume, and cutting and sewing. Costume Makers often move up the costume department career ladder to become a Costume Supervisor.

Stage Jobs Pro member Eleanor Moss is a Costume Maker. We asked her the following questions about her career:

What is the most rewarding aspect of working as a Costume Maker?
Getting to see your costume on the stage, on film or at an event, knowing the costume you made enhanced the character making them come alive.

What are the key skills required to be an effective Costume Maker?
Advanced knowledge in the construction methods of costume making, together with excellent finishing skills. Able to work quickly and efficiently independently, as well as part of a group.

Do you see your role as a natural step on a career ladder, and if so what is the next rung?
Yes as I am currently a freelance maker, I am making the contacts in order to provide myself with continuous work with the companies I am working with. By building up my clientele this will provide me with a steady amount of work. To further my career, I can build on my contacts and get myself fully known within the industry with a good reputation in order to get more work with bigger and better companies. Once I have enough experience as a maker I could also go on to become a wardrobe mistress, cutter or maker within companies.

How did you work your way into your current role?
I studied and gained a BA (Hons) degree in Costume Production at Rose Bruford college, from there I interned at Angels Costumiers to gain more experience within a costume store. I also applied for another internship, where my details were forwarded on to a well known entertainments company to make them several costumes for different events. Also by displaying my work in a college creative industries fair, I gained important contacts who then went on to offer me freelance work.

How much do you think networking helps towards landing a job in the industry?
Networking is a crucial part of gaining contacts in order to get more work. All of my paid jobs to date have been gained through networking, meeting people and making vital contacts that have then aided me in getting work. By networking it also enables you to get your name known within the industry and get a reputation for yourself.

Do you think you will be working in the industry in the next five years, and if so in what capacity?
I intend to still be working within in the industry for at least the next 5 years, though due to the flexibility of my skills it also enables me to transfer across to other areas of clothes making, including in fashion and restoration and conservation work.

Please describe what a typical day working as a Costume Maker might contain?
Talking with a designer or company to determine a design for a costume, deciding on a design, or going fabric sampling. Drafting patterns once designs and fabrics have been confirmed. Cutting fabrics, making up the costume.

Have you done any additional training courses to further your career?
A two day beginners shoe making course. Taking on internships and work experience placements in order to gain more experience on the field.

How important is working for free at the beginning of your career?
Very important, it's a great way to gain more experience which is crucial at the beginning of your career. Again it's another way to get your name known in the industry and it shows you are keen to work hard, shows hunger, drive and determination to succeed despite being not paid.

Costume Cutter
The Costume Cutter assists the Costume Maker and Costume Designer by cutting patterns out of cloth, from which to make the costumes. The Costume Cutter can progress to work as a Costume Designer or Costume Maker.

Costume Supervisor
The Costume Supervisor is the head of the Costume department and as such they are responsible for managing budgets and deadlines, overseeing their team of Costume Assistants or Designers, and liaising with other departments.

Stage Jobs Pro member Richard Gellar is a Costume Supervisor. We asked him the following questions about his career:

What is the most rewarding aspect of working as a Costume Supervisor?
Realising the designer's designs. Coming in under budget and seeing a successful show, with great reviews.

What are the key skills required to be an effective Costume Supervisor?
Budgets, managing staff, organisational skills, costume cutting, period costume history, excellent contacts.

Do you see your role as a natural step on a career ladder, and if so what is the next rung?
Having worked as a Costumier with various teaching and part time admin/management roles, I decided to combine these skills which have allowed me a very successful career. The next step hopefully is costume design or design assistant.

How did you work your way into your current role?
A combination of careers, of which the key one was in costume making, dyeing and breaking down, then working in management part time, having skills in budgets and managing staff. I combined these roles.

How much do you think networking helps towards landing a job in the industry?
For me networking is key, meeting designers and production managers is key for any successful costume supervisor. If you're lucky you can become permanent in a production theatre.

Do you think you will be working in the industry in the next five years, and if so in what capacity?
Hopefully and ideally in the next 5 years I'll have a few designer credits to my name and Film/TV credits.

Please describe what a typical day working as a Costume Supervisor might contain?
Checking and replying to emails, updating the budget, attending fittings, sourcing costumes, touching base with costume makers to ensure deadlines will be met. Liaising with Production Managers and the Designer.

Have you done any additional training courses to further your career?
Only personal choice ones, such as tailoring and millinery.

How important is working for free at the beginning of your career?
Only working for free for the first couple of credits and then making sure that you get paid for the rest. If you are competent and confident in your profession you should be paid for your skills.

77

USEFUL ORGANISATIONS

The Society of British Theatre Designers – *www.theatredesign.org.uk*

COSTUME COURSES IN THE UK

BA (Hons) Costume Construction – Central School of Speech & Drama
www.qurl.com/cssdcost
BA (Hons) Costume Production – Rose Bruford College
www.qurl.com/rosecost
BA (Hons) Costume for Performance – London College of Fashion
www.qurl.com/londonc
PG Dip Theatre Design (Set & Costume) – Royal Academy of Dramatic Art
www.qurl.com/radacost
PG Dip Theatre Costume – Royal Academy of Dramatic Art
www.qurl.com/radapg
Set and Costume Design for the Theatre – Royal Academy of Dramatic Art
www.qurl.com/radasetc
BA (Hons) Theatre: Costume Design – Wimbledon School of Art
www.qurl.com/wimcost
BA (Hons) Theatre: Costume Interpretation – Wimbledon School of Art
www.qurl.com/wimcosti
FdA Costume for Theatre, Television and Film (Two year) – Bristol Old Vic
Theatre School
www.qurl.com/bristfda
BA (Hons) Costume Design & Making – Nottingham Trent University
www.qurl.com/nottcost
BA (Hons) Costume with Performance Design – The Arts Institute at Bournemouth
www.qurl.com/aubccost
BA (Hons) Costume Design and Construction – Queen Margaret University
www.qurl.com/qmucost
Foundation Degree Costume Design and Realisation – Northbrook College
www.qurl.com/northcos
BA (Hons) Costume with Textiles – Huddersfield University
www.qurl.com/hudcost
MA Costume – Huddersfield University
www.qurl.com/hudcosma
FdA Costume Design and Interpretation – Hull College
www.qurl.com/hullcost

Storytelling with Costume and Make-up

THIS GUIDE WAS KINDLY WRITTEN BY NATALIE BROWN, THE PROGRAMME DIRECTOR FOR PERFORMANCE AT LONDON COLLEGE OF FASHION

When the curtain goes up, or the opening film credits pass, the audience is transported into a different world. The opening visual image you see has been carefully constructed to allow you to quickly understand the world and the character that inhabits it. You are introduced to the character with subtle clues that indicate who they are, what job they do, how old they are, what social class they are, what their mood is and what their psychological and physical state is. You make assumptions about their personality, emotions and their history within the first scene. All of this information is passed on, seemingly without the audience even noticing that these visual clues have registered.

Costume and make-up designers collaborate with the director, production designer and actors to help to tell the story to an audience. Firstly, the designer will work with the director and production designer to understand the overall vision of the piece. Having a shared understanding of the character's histories and the style of the piece will enable them to create and realise characters that will come to life and are believable, look right and 'fit'. You don't always notice a good costume or make-up design, but you always notice a bad one. Costume and make-up designers are part of the storytelling toolbox, and the story for the designer always begins with character.

The designers will study the script, calculating who is in each scene, what happens and when it happens. They will also make detailed research into the world the character inhabits, the location and time period. The designers

"Costume and make-up designers collaborate with the director, production designer and actors to help to tell the story to an audience"

will need to know every detail about each character and their story, who says what about each character and what clues the script offers about their personality. The characters will become like best friends, every habit, every detail religiously studied.

Research gathering for a character is one of the most exciting parts of design. When you first read a script you may have some ideas, but like a foggy dream, you can not always see the piece clearly. You need to go out and discover the character, and you can't do this by working with your imagination alone. You need to search, gather and explore.

For your primary research, you may need to visit galleries, relevant locations; you may need to draw from objects or paintings looking for colour, textures, and shapes. You could interview people, collect interesting fabrics and textures. Another good source is vintage clothing and fabrics from charity shops or jumble sales. Unpick the clothes to understand how they are created. You could embody the character, live their life, visit the places they would visit, shop where they would shop, eat and drink where they would, observe and photograph people.

For secondary research you could look at personal photographs, read first hand written accounts, seek out pictures of social life and entertainment events, watch documentaries, read historical text books and descriptions in literary publications, look at postcards, newspapers or satirical cartoons from the period. Magazines are a fantastic source for both contemporary and period advertisements and articles. These will give you clues to what products were available to buy. Portrait paintings will give you clues for colour, style, texture and silhouette as well as hair and make-up of the day. Look at antiques sales catalogues, social event information, posters, archives; what were the available products and dyes? What was happening in politics, science and industry?

You need to become a people watcher and observer to understand the identity and story clues we all emit. Next time you are on train, look at the person opposite you. What are they wearing, how do they wear their hair, why do they wear their coat like that? Is that bangle a gift? What does that brown stain on their left elbow come from? Create a story around the person. Who are they, where have they been? How do you know?

Once all of the research is gathered, you can start to inhabit the world of your characters and start to build an image of what they may look like in each scene. What sort of shoes would they wear? What colour would they choose? Why have they chosen that? What have they done before they arrive in the scene?

Actors play a large part in your design process. You are collaborating with them to create a believable person. You may want to restrict their movements to enhance the character, or you may need to add padding to create a different silhouette. (But it's no good designing a huge brim on a hat if you can't see their face!) Your actor has to feel comfortable and has to leave the dressing room feeling completely at ease, stress free and ready to perform and inhabit the character.

As a costume or make-up designer you have to have oodles of patience. You need to be able to listen carefully and be prepared to negotiate and compromise. The role requires collaboration skills within a team as you will never be working in isolation.

Choose a book or a play, and start to create your own character design using your own investigative research.

The guide was kindly written by Natalie Brown, the Programme Director for Performance at London College of Fashion. London College of Fashion offers performance design degrees in costume, technical effects and make-up. For more information please go to **www.fashion.arts.ac.uk/courses** or call on **+44 (0)20 7514 7344**.

Make-up Artist

Make-up Artists use face paint, body paint, prosthetics, and cosmetics to create visual effects and looks to suit the characters. They must make-up actors before a production, maintain their make-up during the production, and then remove the make-up afterwards. They will often work with the Director to design a make-up scheme that enhances the play. Make-up Artists may also be expected to deal with hair-dressing for the actors.

National Association of Screen Make-up Artists & Hairdressers – Careers Advice

THIS GUIDE HAS BEEN REPRODUCED IN ITS ENTIRETY WITH KIND PERMISSION FROM NASMAH

NASMAH Life as a professional make-up artist is hard, erratic, challenging, exciting, varied – and extremely competitive! Even the most thorough training does not guarantee success.

Make-up career

So you want to be a make-up artist?

Many people unfortunately assume that being a make-up artist will lead to a glamorous future. However, the hours and work conditions, in most cases, are long and hard – and even the most thorough training cannot ensure a successful career. Competition for jobs is fierce and there are only so many industry jobs out there. Despite all this, you may wish to find out more.

What areas to work in?

There are different areas in the media in which a make-up artist can work: film, television, theatre, editorial, fashion and so on. Some areas are similar, and some are quite different and require different training, though the core skills and elements (like health and safety) are the same.

An overview of the job

The hair and make-up department is responsible for the design, application, continuity and care of hair and make-up during a production. It ensures that actors, performers, presenters, models and others have suitable make-up and hairstyles before they appear in front of the cameras or an audience (be it for television, film, theatre, catwalk or photographic) and that the looks are maintained.

Some productions or types of work have separate hair and make-up departments, but for many jobs you would be expected to have both hair and make-up skills. There are also specialist areas like body painting, wig making, prosthetics, making contact lenses and making teeth.

Key skills

These are just some of the key skills and attributes you need to be a good make-up artist:

- Make-up skills including corrective, glamour, period and ageing;
- Specialised techniques e.g. making and applying bald caps; applying and dressing facial hair; creating casualty effects (burns, skin diseases, cuts, scars etc.); tattoos and body art;
- Hair and wig dressing;
- Continuity hair cutting;
- Good communication and diplomacy skills;
- Good organisational and presentation skills;
- Ability to work effectively as part of a team as well as having initiative when working unsupervised;
- Ability to work under pressure to external and departmental deadlines;
- The right attitude and work ethic;
- Willingness to work long and often unsocial hours;
- Knowledge of the relevant Health and Safety legislation and procedures – and good working practices and hygiene.

Training & Experience

To start down the road of becoming a media make-up artist:

- completing a good foundation training course in media make-up is important;
- getting good on-the-job experience and training is vital.

Hairdressing is also an important skill for most areas of make-up. Completing an NVQ in hairdressing is advisable.

How do I find a course?

There are lots of foundation courses out there. With a little persistence and research you should find the right one for you. The NASMAH website has a "Find a Course" section for further help and guidance.

Who runs make-up courses?

As an association we do not endorse or

"Life as a professional make-up artist is hard, erratic, challenging, exciting, varied – and extremely competitive!"

recommend any school or college. Many of our members run their own courses and private schools advertise courses in most women's and fashion magazines (and these courses are not subsidised). Many Local Authority colleges run media courses which often include both make-up and hairdressing.

What to look for in a course

Make-up artistry and hairdressing are hands-on professions and, therefore, have to be taught in a classroom environment:

- Live models should be used (even if you just practice on each other) for as much of the course as possible.
- Tutors should be readily on hand to offer guidance, assistance and criticism.
- Important! Look at what the tutors have done within the industry itself. Many may be qualified to teach, but do they have proper and substantial industry experience?

Doing a course does not guarantee you a career in make-up! Some colleges do not emphasise how hard it often is to get (and keep getting) work and may even promise you a glittering career if you train with them. NO ONE can guarantee this.

Career path

Doing a make-up course does not make you a make-up artist! There is career progression and it takes time to gain the right experience to progress.

After completing a foundation training course, you are a trainee. There is much for you to learn, not only about hair and make-up but about how a production works, set etiquette, continuity and so on – things that a course can only teach in theory.

After being a trainee you progress to being an assistant and, after several years of solid experience, you may then be considered a make-up artist.

Being a film or television make-up designer takes many years of experience and NASMAH cannot stress this enough – simply doing a make-up course does not make you a designer! You never stop learning and developing your skills.

This guide has been reproduced in its entirety with kind permission from NASMAH. NASMAH is a professional, social and educational organisation who encourage the highest standards in the craft of media hair and make-up, and work hard to promote their members. You can find more information at **www.nasmah.co.uk**

USEFUL ORGANISATIONS

NASMAH (National Association of Screen Make-up Artists and Hairdressers) – ***www.nasmah.co.uk***. A lot of useful information can be found on their website and they have a page providing careers advice to aspiring make-up artists at www.qurl.com/nasmah.

MAKE UP COURSES IN THE UK

BA (Hons) Make-up for Media and Performance – The Arts University College Bournemouth
www.qurl.com/aucbmu
Foundation Degree Make-up & Hairstyling for Theatre Arts – Northbrook College
www.qurl.com/northmu
BA (Hons) Make up & Prosthetics for Performance – London College of Fashion
www.qurl.com/londonmu
TV, Film, and Theatre Make-up – Greasepaint
www.qurl.com/greasetft
5* Make-up Course – Greasepaint
www.qurl.com/greasestar
Higher Education Certificate in Professional Make-up Design – Delamar Academy
www.qurl.com/delhe
Advanced Complete Make-up Artist – Delamar Academy
www.qurl.com/deladv
Complete Make-up Artist – Delamar Academy
www.qurl.com/delcomp
Media Make-up – School of Make-ups
www.qurl.com/mediamu
The following organisations also run regular make up courses:
The Academy of Make-up, Glasgow –
www.theacademyofmakeup.com/index.html
Central Saint Martins College of Arts and Design, London –
www.csm.arts.ac.uk/shortcourses
Westminster Adult Education Services, London – www.waes.ac.uk
Stockport College – ***www.stockport.ac.uk***
Brushstroke – ***www.brushstroke.co.uk***
DFMA – ***www.makeupacademy.co.uk***

Job Types

Wigs Assistant
The Wigs Assistant helps the other members of the wig department to prepare wigs, maintain them during the performance, and then remove and prep them for the following performance. They may progress to work as Wig Dresser, Wig Supervisor, or Wig Maker.

Wig Maker
The Wig Maker creates wigs for a performance. They are responsible for liaising with the Director and Costume Designer, and doing any necessary research to ensure that the wigs are appropriate to the production.

Wig Supervisor
The Wig Supervisor (also known as the Wig Master/Mistress) is the head of the wig department, and so manages the team of Wig Makers, Wig Assistants, and Wig Dressers. They are responsible for communication between the wig department and the rest of the production, supervising wig repairs and adjustments, maintaining wigs during the performance for the lead roles, and collecting wigs at the end in preparation for the next show.

Stage Jobs Pro member Linzi Bowen is a Wig Mistress. We asked her the following questions about her career:

What is the most rewarding aspect of working as a Wig Mistress?
The most rewarding aspect is to manage a fantastic team on a great show. And to be involved in the creative process, with the Designer, on a brand new production.

What are the key skills required to be an effective Wig Mistress?
The key skills required to be an effective Wig Mistress are utilising your professional training and prior experience to confidently manage a team. Following a thorough training period, steadily working up from an Assistant to Deputy Wig Mistress, then enables you to develop the skills required to competently become the Head of Wigs Department.

Do you see your role as a natural step on a career ladder, and if so what is the next rung?
Usually a Wigs Mistress would progress to becoming a Wigs Supervisor then Designer. However, as making wigs is not my primary skill, this is not a career path that I would chose to pursue. For me the next step, having now spent many years working in Theatre, is to establish a career in TV, where I am more likely to be able to utilise my

skills in both hair and make-up, rather than just predominantly in wigs.

How did you work your way into your current role?

Initially, I trained as a Hairdresser/Beauty Therapist, working in this field for a year before making the decision to focus instead on becoming involved in Theatre and TV, as a Hair/Make-up Artist. I lined up work experience at my local theatres, studied Art and Biology A' Levels then went on to complete a HND course at The London College of Fashion in Specialist Make-up.

After graduating, I was employed as a Wig Assistant by the Royal Shakespeare Company for a 6 month season, enabling me to gain valuable experience, from senior artists, in working with hair, wigs, make-up and special effects before then embarking on a career in the West End.

After several years working in London, progressing from Wig Assistant to Deputy, I elected to travel and work overseas in Australia, where I landed my dream job at Sydney Opera House.

When I eventually returned to the UK, to resume my career in London, I periodically worked with the RSC, enlisted some TV work and managed the Wigs Department on several West End Musicals, Plays and Touring Productions.

In more recent years, I have worked as a Wigs Tutor, ventured back into a career in TV and spent a season working at Glyndebourne Opera Festival.

How much do you think networking helps towards landing a job in the industry?

I do think that networking helps towards landing a job in the industry, although it is not something that I readily engage in. However, it is a very competitive field, with more and more training schools opening thus more graduates each year competing for the best jobs. Therefore, contacts are vital, especially in the early stages of your career.

Do you think you will be working in the industry in the next five years, and if so in what capacity?

Yes absolutely. Most likely on a freelance basis in Theatre, Opera and TV, both here and overseas, having recently returned from a year in South America establishing contacts there, for future employment. I would also like to pursue more teaching opportunities.

Please describe what a typical day working as a Wig Supervisor might contain?

A typical day working as a Wigs Mistress involves managing the department and liaising with the other Department Heads in preparation for the next performance. Additional responsibilities could include providing wigs/make-up for an Understudy performance or publicity shoot, scheduling wig fittings for a cast change and arranging haircuts for the cast. And generally, to oversee the daily wig maintenance, schedule working hours/holiday and to monitor any stock requirements for the production.

Working hours vary depending on the scale of the production and are largely determined by the level of maintenance required of any given day. Typically, on a normal show day the department may start at 1pm and work through until curtain down. On a matinee day, 11am is an average start time, with a 10.30pm finish. The majority of West End productions have a working week Monday through to Saturday, 8 shows per week with 2 matinees. Though in more recent years, a production may include a Sunday performance, rather than a Monday.

Initially, when a production is set up, the Wig Mistress allocates wigs to each member of the team to be responsible for maintaining on a daily basis. At the start of the working day, the wigs are cleaned and assessed to see if they require redressing or resetting. Checks are made for any repairs that may be required. Any wigs that require washing and resetting are done first to allow time for them to dry and take the set/style. The rest of the wigs are then redressed until everything is ready for the next performance.

The Wig Mistress traditionally tends to look after the lead actors and will therefore be responsible for preparing them for the show, while the Deputy and Assistant(s) cover the Ensemble members of the acting company. During the half hour call, the actors are prepped for their wigs or alternatively their own hair is styled.

Once the show is up and running, the team along with a member of the Wardrobe Department, follow their cue sheet/track notes to cover any changes to the appearance of their designated actors. At the end of the performance, the wigs are all collected up and returned to the department to be prepared for the next day.

Have you done any additional training courses to further your career?
Yes. I try to incorporate additional training courses whenever I'm between jobs. As it's a fair few years since I graduated from LCF, I polish up my skills periodically with short refresher courses. I see this as an essential method of keeping up to date with developments in the industry, therefore ensuring that I am as employable as possible.

How important is working for free at the beginning of your career?
I don't necessarily agree that working for free is important at the beginning of your career, rather that you try to gain as much experience as possible, unpaid or otherwise, before approaching established organisations for employment. For example, there are numerous websites that advertise for crew for short films etc. While these positions are often unpaid or low pay, they can potentially offer a fantastic opportunity to gain valuable experience and develop contacts for future work. With the benefit of work experience, newcomers to the industry can certainly improve their

chances of securing employment in their chosen field.

However in the first instance, I firmly believe that choosing the right training school is the most significant priority. Some are more established than others and careful consideration should always be given when selecting the one you wish to attend. If possible, visit the school beforehand and speak with the tutors. Check what courses are offered and what facilities are available.

Obviously the financial costs of training must also be factored into the choice and whether that dictates a preference for a short course of a few weeks/months or a longer course with the training offered over one or two years. Each method of study has positive and negative aspects. But as someone who has worked in the industry for a considerable number of years, I can honestly say that the required skills are not learned overnight. A certificate is no match for experience. So wherever you choose, choose wisely.

WIGS COURSES IN THE UK

Beginner's "Taster" Course – The Wig Academy
www.qurl.com/thewigac
Wig Making (3 months) – The Wig Academy
www.qurl.com/wigthree
Intensive Wig Dressing (3 months) – The Wig Academy
www.qurl.com/wiginten
Wig Dressing (1 month) – The Wig Academy
www.qurl.com/wigone
Wig Making – City & Guilds
www.qurl.com/citywig

Job Types

Wardrobe Assistant

Wardrobe Assistants have various roles in producing and maintaining costumes, sewing, cutting, altering, and mending costumes, and assisting the wardrobe department. Wardrobe Assistants will often progress to work as Wardrobe Mistress/Master.

Stage Jobs Pro member Madeline Taylor is a Wardrobe Assistant. We asked her the following questions about her career:

What is the most rewarding aspect of working as a Wardrobe Assistant?

The most rewarding aspect is helping pull the show together, working with pretty much everyone, actor, director, designer, makers, to come up with the best costume for the character and context. It can be a heap of paperwork and admin, but it can also be a heap of fun and a large variety of different small jobs.

What are the key skills required to be an effective Wardrobe Assistant?

Being organized (and the ability to know where your organizational skills will fail, and planning for this to circumvent them). Being able to get along with everyone, and the patience (and the ability to hold your tongue) that this sometimes requires. An eye for the small details that make a costume complete.

Do you see your role as a natural step on a career ladder, and if so what is the next rung?

I have moved up, down and sideways on the costuming rungs a few times, but the ability to be a good Wardrobe Assistant will be a great step in anyone's career. If you are working on a big enough project, after seeing a few of these through (depending on their duration of course) you should feel comfortable to start coordinating small shows in your own right.

How did you work your way into your current role?

I was lucky enough to complete a Wardrobe Traineeship with a profes-sional theatre company, which got me in the door and a year's experience and industry knowledge.

How much do you think networking helps towards landing a job in the industry?

Lots! But please don't do it obviously, and choose your timing wisely! Your best bet may be giving the person who can help you your card and asking them to call you (maybe working for free) if they get swamped. Hopefully this will happen in the next few weeks and you will be able to help them when they are stuck. Thats a really good way to be remembered (as long as you are actually helpful!)

Do you think you will be working in the industry in the next five years, and if so in what capacity?
I am hoping to be working on smaller independent projects with more creative focus, and interspersing this with academic research into costume and society.

Please describe what a typical day working as a Wardrobe Assistant might contain?
Arrive at 8ish, confer with the Head of Wardrobe about tasks for the day, prep for any fittings or meetings of the day, make a heap of phone calls organising supplies, hires, haberdashery, staff, suppliers; attend a fitting or production meeting and take lots of notes, assist the makers or cutters with any issues they are having, have lunch, head out shopping, hurry back for fitting, have a brief meeting with designer, put stuff away, answer emails.

Have you done any additional training courses to further your career?
Yes, but on the job experience is far more valuable.

How important is working for free at the beginning of your career?
Fairly important as it exposes you to new workrooms, but make sure this is not taken advantage of. You shouldn't work more than one week for free for any company that can afford to pay you, unless you know absolutely nothing (or it's for uni/assessment)

Madeline's website is **www.theloop.com.au/madeline-taylor**.

Wardrobe Manager

The Wardrobe Manager manages the costume department, budgeting, organising laundry, managing a team of Wardrobe Assistants, and communicating with other departments.

© COLETTE PADOVANI

Stage Jobs Pro member Zoe Baron is a Wardrobe Manager. We asked her the following questions about her career:

What is the most rewarding aspect of working as a Wardrobe Manager?

It ranges from working with great designers to create beautiful costumes, to a small alteration or purchase that will make the actors/artists feel comfortable and confident on stage.

What are the key skills required to be an effective Wardrobe Manager?

A photographic memory! Perhaps not as extreme as that but you do have to remember a lot of details of costume change, rehearsal notes, designers and directors comments, ordering... To help you with this, organisation is key – you can never be too organised! You need to be able to communicate well and listen to others, and always try to remain calm – on the surface at least! Above all you have to be able to effectively delegate work, and to always be approachable to your staff. They are wanting to get the job done right and quickly too, if this

is a problem them look to yourself before loading the blame on your workers.

Do you see your role as a natural step on a career ladder, and if so what is the next rung?

Wardrobe Manager or Costume Supervisor is in a way the highest you can go in regards to the Wardrobe Department in Theatre. Designing is really a different job entirely, but it is in some respects the next step up. Also there is always work in Film and TV to consider, where the work is different but the skills of a Wardrobe Manager would be valued. This may be considered more of a side step than a step up, but it would still be a valuable experience.

How did you work your way into your current role?

I didn't follow the typical degree route to get into Theatre. I worked voluntarily with local Theatre groups from the age of 17. I attended a Costume degree course at 19 but quit after one year as I was unimpressed with the course and I had found myself a Wardrobe Assistant position. Since then I have gradually worked my way up to Wardrobe Manager and Designer. I would argue that a degree is relatively useless and a waste of money. If you are keen and are willing to work for free for a little while you will learn far more and most importantly you will be making contacts. In the entertainment industry, more than any other I feel, contacts are your most important ally.

How much do you think networking helps towards landing a job in the industry?

Massively. Always take care to network as much as possible. You never know who you might meet and who may have a job for you.

Do you think you will be working in the industry in the next five years, and if so in what capacity?

I'm not sure! Theatre and TV/Film are all consuming jobs – consider it a vocation – and when you start to crave a life outside it you really have to consider which is most important to you. I'm not sure that in five years my job will be the top of my list of priorities, and to be honest it is difficult to do this job well and not make it your priority.

Please describe what a typical day working as a Wardrobe Manager might contain?

Days vary massively, but here is an example of a tech week schedule (not a touring or established production). Generally in work for 9am. Checking of orders, ordering and important emails must be done first. At 10.00am the cast will start coming in. By this time all the dressing rooms should be ready for their arrival, and if this is not the case it is all hands on deck to get

things done in time. After 10.00 but before teching begins on stage, go round all the dressing rooms to check that everyone has everything. Go up to the Wardrobe Department and delegate finding/making of the desired items to your staff members. Check all staff are happy with their set tasks and then head down to tech rehearsal. Throughout the day sit with the designer and take notes of desired changes regarding Wardrobe. If there are Dressers working on the production, check they are aware of any changes and on occasion oversee any quick changes that are causing problems. 10.00pm Go home! There are generally some gaps to grab food but it is certainly not unheard of to go an entire day living on snatched biscuits and scalding coffee!

Have you done any additional training courses to further your career?

I haven't done any additional training courses but many interest me and I hope to perhaps be able to attend some in future.

How important is working for free at the beginning of your career?

Very important. As I said earlier, I would recommend working for free for a year rather than doing a three year degree. It will leave you with less debt and will be vastly more profitable to you in the future.

Set Design & Scenery

Scenic Artist

The Scenic Artist paints and decorates all parts of the set, working from a scale model to make the set identical to the set design produced by the Set Designer. Time may be spent working from the Set Designer's plans, mixing colours, and testing textures to get the best effect. The Production Manager then signs it off.

Set Designer

Set Designers design a scale model or scale drawings, which are then used by the Set Builder to create that set. They may also spend time sourcing materials, doing research, liaising with the Director and making adjustments.

Stage Jobs Pro member Bek Palmer is a Set Designer. We asked her the following questions about her career:

What is the most rewarding aspect of working as a Set Designer?
It is a hugely creative job and has the benefit of always being a collaboration with other inspiring people. It is also fantastic to see your ideas become a reality in the end and see other people inhabit your creations and bring new ideas, doing something unexpected with what you have given them.

What are the key skills required to be an effective Set Designer?
Communication, through many mediums, conversations, drawings, models.

Do you see your role as a natural step on a career ladder, and if so what is the next rung?
Yes, it has taken a long time to make the step up to this from fringe theatre. I would like the next step to be productions where there are proper departments to work with to realise my designs.

How did you work your way into your current role?
I studied Theatre Design at degree level and then worked in youth theatre and community theatre designing alongside working as a propmaker and wardrobe mistress to support myself. I then went back to college to retrain at postgrad level as I didn't feel my traditional design skills were at the same level as other people at my stage in their career. I then began in London designing for fringe theatre and assisting established designers. Through contacts made during this

period I got involved with larger theatre companies as an assistant and then designer.

How much do you think networking helps towards landing a job in the industry?

I feel it is essential. Other than one design job which I got through the traditional interview process, all jobs have come through people I have met on other jobs or met whilst networking.

Do you think you will be working in the industry in the next five years, and if so in what capacity?

I hope to still be working as a designer but more established.

Please describe what a typical day working as a Set Designer might contain?

It is hugely varied. It could be researching a particular period, or other artist's work, or making 1:25 scale furniture, or drawing ideas for characters, making a puppet, filming something for projections... every day seems to be different which is one of the great parts of the job.

Have you done any additional training courses to further your career?

Well, I did the Postgraduate Diploma in Theatre Design at RWCMD five year after my degree. I also did a short course in Puppetry and object manipulation as that is my specialist area of interest. I often take part in drawing courses to regularly improve my skills there.

How important is working for free at the beginning of your career?

I have found it really useful in some cases and it has led to paid work. This is not always the case. It is only useful to do free work as long as you are gaining experience or making contacts. Some jobs have felt they do neither of these and are just taking advantage of free labour. In these cases it is best not to continue with this for too long as it is preventing you from doing something more beneficial.

USEFUL ORGANISATIONS
The Society of British Theatre Designers – *www.theatredesign.org.uk*

SET DESIGN COURSES IN THE **UK**
PG Dip Theatre Design (Set & Costume) – Royal Academy of Dramatic Art
www.qurl.com/radades
BA (Hons) Theatre and Screen – Theatre Design – Wimbledon School of Art
www.qurl.com/wimdesign
BA (Hons) Scenic Art – Central School of Speech & Drama
www.qurl.com/cssdsa
BA (Hons) Scenic Art – Rose Bruford College
www.qurl.com/rosesa
MA Scenic Art and Construction for Stage and Screen – The Royal Welsh
College of Music and Drama
www.qurl.com/rwcmdsa
Scenic Art – Royal Academy of Dramatic Art
www.qurl.com/radasa
PG Dip Scenic Art – Bristol Old Vic Theatre School
www.qurl.com/oldvicsa

Carpenter

Carpenters work with wood to create stage components, props, and set. They may work in a workshop to create the wooden elements, or on-site making adjustments. Possible career progression includes working on a contract at a theatre as the inhouse Deputy Master Carpenter, Master Carpenter or Head of Construction.

CARPENTRY COURSES IN THE **UK**
Carpentry and Joinery (CAA Diploma) – City & Guilds
www.qurl.com/citycar
Carpentry and Joinery – Hackney Community College
www.qurl.com/hackcar
Introductory Carpentry Course – Able Skills
www.qurl.com/ablecar
Carpentry Courses – The Building Crafts College
www.qurl.com/build

Set Builder

The Set Builder uses the designs of the Set Designer to create props and set components, and are responsible for making any necessary changes. They are also often required to contact suppliers and order materials. As well as having practical skills, the Set Builder needs to be very good at time management, so as to be able to build multiple pieces to schedule and make changes to the set at short notice.

SCENIC CONSTRUCTION COURSES IN THE UK
BA (Hons) Scenic Construction – Central School of Speech & Drama
www.qurl.com/cssdsc
MA Scenic Art and Construction for Stage and Screen – The Royal Welsh College of Music and Drama
www.qurl.com/rwcmdsa
Scenic Construction – Royal Academy of Dramatic Art
www.qurl.com/radasc

Prop Maker

Prop Makers create props for the production, working alongside the Set Designer, Scenic Artist and Production Manager. They are responsible for ensuring that the cost of the props is within budget, and that the props are appropriate to the production design. Prop Makers may specialise, but they are expected to have a wide range of technical and artistic skills.

Stage Jobs Pro member Chiok Li is a Prop Maker. We asked him the follow questions about his career:

goal, it is the stage where a person will be hands on and responsible for the build. Like an artist, it is your hand that shapes it and will always be your work. There are further roles: propmaster, standby props or managing a property warehouse, but you will always want to be the person making the things.

What is the most rewarding aspect of working as a Prop Maker?

Working on some of the most interesting and detailed aspects of a film shoot. Good props make a story seem possible and great props make it come to life. Anything that is handled is a prop and most of the time they will be generic everyday items. But every so often you'll get the opportunity to design and make something that no one will have ever seen before and that is the greatest reward.

What are the key skills required to be an effective Prop Maker?

A diverse mixture of fabrication skills and an awareness of techniques are required to recognise how a design on paper can be realised into a 3D object. So learn the basics of wood, metal, fibreglass, sculpting, casting, material knowledge, painting etc. Experience will come when you can look at a drawing and identify what materials and processes can be used to create it. Being good with a hot glue gun always helps.

Do you see your role as a natural step on a career ladder, and if so what is the next rung?

A prop maker can be seen as the

How did you work your way into your current role?

I came into the role sideways from a degree in mechanical engineering. Using the engineering skills I had and learning new skills in my own time, I created a variety of props and models to demonstrate my skills and compiled a portfolio which I show to employers as an example of my abilities. I always enjoyed making things and watching films so it was nice that there is a job which combines the two.

How much do you think networking helps towards landing a job in the industry?

Pretty much essential. If you work freelance for yourself, you need to be on people's radar to have work offered to you. Employers will only advertise crew positions if they don't already have the right person in mind. So it should be your aim to be the right person for their job and show them the portfolio and how you can benefit the production. It always helps to be in the front of others minds when they think a prop needs making. Having business cards and a website will always help. The other option is to work for a props production company. Most employees are still freelance but work on the projects acquired by the company who generally have more power in gaining contracts and so work is more constant. The downside is that you won't always get individual credit and see the final product to the end.

Do you think you will be working in the industry in the next five years, and if so in what capacity?

I hope to always be making things in some capacity and with greater experience comes bigger and more impressive jobs. Working freelance has the benefits of freedom but no assurance of constant work so the other goal would be to become a production manager for a props warehouse where you would be responsible for other prop makers but still create things from time to time with the safety of a salary.

Please describe what a typical day working as a Prop Maker might contain.

Liaise with the clients over their opinions and decisions for the designs and how the manufacturing process is progressing. Constant communication is required to ensure that everyone is happy with the finished product and you deliver the specified item. Generally working in a studio or workshop and continuing with the fabrication according to the plan. Planning out the work so you spend the day moulding or sculpting or painting and then leaving things at the end of the day to dry or harden so you can return the next day and continue working on it.

Have you done any additional training courses to further your career?

A lot of the work provides its own experience and training and working with other prop makers is a great opportunity to pick up new skills. There are courses and degree programmes which will teach these skills in a credited environment but as long as you can demonstrate the same skills in your own way, only the results matter.

How important is working for free at the beginning of your career?

If you are working freelance for yourself, very important. Props are an often neglected aspect of a production and expected to be created with minimum hassle. As long as your expenses are covered, the experience of dealing with clients and their specifications is the experience to take from the project. If an unpaid work experience programme extends further than three months, then you are being taken advantage of. Working for a production company will generally always get paid if you can complete the work as they require it so signing on with a company is a good way to gain experience and get paid.

Prop Manager

The Prop Manager is in charge of the props team, managing the Prop Maker, Props Assistant, and Props Buyer. They are responsible for supervising the development, creation, purchase, rental and use of props.

Books on Prop Making

Stage Design and Properties, Michael Holt, 1993

Scenic Art for the Theatre, Susan Crabtree, 2012

Stage Design: A Practical Guide, Gary Thorne, 1999

Scenic Art and Construction: A Practical Guide, Tim Blaikie, Emma Troubridge, 2002

The Stage Guide to working in craft and construction, Susan Elkin, 2008

Prop Making Courses in the UK

BA (Hons) Prop Making – Central School of Speech & Drama

www.qurl.com/cssdprop

Property Making – Royal Academy of Dramatic Art

www.qurl.com/radaprop

Property Making for the Stage: An Introduction – Royal Academy of Dramatic Art

www.qurl.com/radapi

Foundation Degree Production Design/Prop Making – Northbrook College

www.qurl.com/northprop

Puppet Builder

Puppet Builders are responsible for developing and making puppets for performances. They may combine this with being a puppeteer.

Useful Organisations

The British Puppet & Model Theatre Association –

www.puppetguild.org.uk

Directing, Producing & Choreography

Director's Assistant
The Director's Assistant works with the Director to achieve their artistic vision. The Director's Assistant takes care of administrative duties, runs errands, and assists the Director in rehearsals. They may progress to the role of Director.

Director
Directors are responsible for bringing a play from the page to the stage: directing the actors, managing the crew, and developing a creative vision for the play. Directors must be excellent communicators, good at managing people, adept at problem-solving and very creative.

© DAVID PRICE PHOTOGRAPHY

Stage Jobs Pro member Andrew Hobbs is a Director. We asked him the following questions about his career:

What is the most rewarding aspect of working as a Director?
When you sit down to watch the first night and see how well a show has come together. Directing isn't for those who want to be in the spotlight or get the credit for a great production – that's for the performers! A good script doesn't automatically translate into a good performance, so the director's job is to act as an effective bridge between the two and the rewards are in taking quiet satisfaction in your work and thinking 'I did that!'

when the crowd give a standing ovation at the end of the show.
What are the key skills required to be an effective Director?
Other than the obvious like a good knowledge of stage composition and the ability to view the production as a whole as well as having an in depth understanding of the individual parts that go into making it, the most important one for me is people skills. To take an example, you'll get a situation where you've been trying to get an actor to do something a certain way for an hour and they're just not getting it, and then suddenly they'll turn round and suggest exactly what you've been trying to explain as if it was their idea. If you're the sort of person who can't resist saying 'I told you so' then directing isn't for you – instead you need to be able to say 'that's a great idea why didn't I think of that?' and move on.

Do you see your role as a natural step on a career ladder, and if so what is the next rung?

I'm passionate about being involved in the creative process for exciting and original theatre be it as director, writer or producer. I suppose the ultimate would be for me to have my own theatre to run where I could programme what I like, with enough funding to ease the commercial pressure of having to sell a large volume of tickets. Maybe one day!

How did you work your way into your current role?

I initially trained in directing, theatre administration, sound design and acting at university. I then went off to do a postgraduate year at drama school and went into acting. From there I became involved in producing and directing, and discovered over time that life backstage was more appealing to me than pursuing a career on it. Having my own theatre company, which I've now had going for 8 years, has given me the freedom to develop all these aspects of my career and get more and more of my writing on the stage.

How much do you think networking helps towards landing a job in the industry?

Love it or hate it, it is probably one of the most important aspects of the industry. From every level right from the tiniest pub theatre to the biggest West End venue, people naturally look to work with people they know, or people they have worked with before who have done a good job, purely for the sake of convenience and reduced risk. So put simply, the more people you know the more work you'll get.

Do you think you will be working in the industry in the next five years, and if so in what capacity?

Definitely. I'll keep my theatre companies Facsimile Productions and British Touring Shakespeare going and also continue to work as a freelance director and writer.

Please describe what a typical day working as a Director might contain?

I'll take that to mean a day of rehearsals. I'd start off by looking through the scenes that are on the schedule that day to gather my thoughts together about them. I try and come into the rehearsal room with a fairly open mind so that I can incorporate the actors' ideas, but at the same time you need to have a clear structure of where you want it to go in your head, so it's important to get a balance. I'd then start the scene rehearsal with a read through of the text, then sit down for a discussion about how the actors see their characters in the scene before getting it up on its feet and making it work. You've then got the slightly more hectic days like tech rehearsals and opening nights, when it's just about keeping a cool head under pressure and making sure you're on top of everything and in control.

Have you done any additional training courses to further your career?

Not since I left drama school. I think there's a certain amount of theory that you can learn, and then like anything it's just about doing it as much as possible and learning on the job. I don't think anyone ever gets to the point where they've got nothing further to learn in their chosen field, but you definitely get better with every job that you do.

How important is working for free at the beginning of your career?

Unless you're very lucky it's pretty much essential. Like any industry, people are chosen on the basis of their experience more than anything else, so you need to get those credits on your CV, and given the general lack of money around the theatre industry at the moment, most of the projects you'll have an opportunity to work on at any one time aren't going to have much funding behind them, so it'll either be low pay or none whatsoever. There are three reasons why you should take a job, which are if it pays well, furthers your career or you'll enjoy doing it. As long as at least two of those are the case then go for it!

You can find out more information about Andrew and his theatre companies, Facsimile Productions and British Touring Shakespeare here:
www.facsimileproductions.co.uk
www.facebook.com/facsimile productions
www.twitter.com/BTSFacsimile

Andrew Loretto wrote this great guide to writing a directing proposal for Get Into Theatre. It's a good introduction to how to approach directing a theatre piece:

How do I write a directing proposal?
THIS ARTICLE HAS BEEN REPRODUCED IN ITS ENTIRETY WITH KIND PERMISSION FROM GET INTO THEATRE
AUTHOR: ANDREW LORETTO, CO-DIRECTOR, CHOL THEATRE, HUDDERSFIELD

There is no set format to writing a directing proposal as it will reflect your personal flair, passions and interests as a director, as well as the particular requirements of that project.

getintotheatre

However, I would suggest that you should always try and get the following basics into any proposal (I'll call the project a 'show' for now – but of course, it could be a play, an event etc.):

1. The title of the show
2. What the show is about
3. Why you want to make the show – why here? Why now?
4. Who you want to make the show with
5. How you envisage making the show
6. Who the show is for (ie. who is the audience?)
7. Your background as a director
8. Your full contact details (you'll be amazed how many people forget this...)

And then, if required and/or useful...

9. Timescale
10. Suggested budget
11. Marketing suggestions
12. CVs of yourself and key artistic personnel, script extracts, photos, images, DVDs, CDs as appropriate
13. A stamped address envelope if you want the material returned when finished with.

Depending on the circumstances, you can write as short or long a pitch as required. But generally speaking, you want to be able to get the main info across in a concise fashion in two pages – a bit like writing a CV or job application.

You can always offer more detail to supplement the initial 'hook' page or pages.

The other thing about a directing pitch is that your creativity and passion should come across on the page – but still with clarity. If you wish, run the pitch past someone who knows nothing about the project to see if it makes sense to them before you send it to theatre companies.

The other thing is, yes it is a sales document, but it needs to be an honest sales document. Please don't pitch a project that you know you can't deliver or is not within your skill set. Be honest about your strengths and play to those.

Good luck!

"*In a directing pitch your creativity and passion should come across on the page – but still with clarity***"**

This article has been reproduced in its entirety with kind permission from Get Into Theatre. Their site hopes to open your eyes to the huge variety of careers in the industry – and the different ways to get there. You can find out more at **www.getintotheatre.org**.

USEFUL ORGANISATIONS

The Directors Guild of Great Britain – *www.dggb.org*

BOOKS ON DIRECTING

Directing A Play, Michael McCaffery, 1988

Theatre Craft: A Director's Practical Companion from A to Z, John Caird, 2010

The Director's Craft: A handbook for the theatre, Katie Mitchell, 2008

DIRECTING COURSES IN THE UK

MA Theatre Directing – Mountview Academy of Theatre Arts

www.qurl.com/mountdir

PG Dip Theatre Directing – Mountview Academy of Theatre Arts

www.qurl.com/mountdpg

BA (Hons) Theatre Arts: Theatre Directing – Middlesex University

www.qurl.com/middled

MA Drama Directing – Bristol Old Vic Theatre School

www.qurl.com/oldvicd

Diploma Course Directors – London Academy of Music and Dramatic Art

www.qurl.com/lamdadir

MA Theatre (Directing) – Royal Holloway, University of London

www.qurl.com/rhuldir

MRes Directing and Dramaturgy – University of Birmingham

www.qurl.com/birmdir

MA/Mfa Theatre Directing – East 15 Acting School

www.qurl.com/eastdir

Directing – City Literary Institute

www.qurl.com/citydir

MA Theatre Direction: Text and Production – University of East Anglia

www.qurl.com/ueadir

MA Theatre Directing – Birkbeck College, University of London

www.qurl.com/birkdec

Casting Assistant

Casting Assistants work with the Casting Director in the process of choosing actors for certain roles. This may involve creating character lists, contacting agents and actors, and assisting with casting sessions. Casting Assistants often have previously worked as Production Assistants, and will naturally progress to the role of Casting Director.

Casting Director

Casting Directors oversee the process of choosing actors for the roles in a production. This involves creating character lists, contacting agents and actors, assisting with casting sessions, and negotiating fees and contracts for actors.

USEFUL ORGANISATIONS
The Casting Directors Guild of Great Britain – *www.thecdg.co.uk*

Choreographer

Choreographers develop, design, and direct movement in the production, working with the Director to ensure that dances and movement sequences fit the creative vision of the performance. Choreographers often come from a dance performance or teaching background. Choreographers must be creative, skilled dancers, and good communicators.

BOOKS ON CHOREOGRAPHY
Choreography, Sandra Cerny Minton, 2007

CHOREOGRAPHY COURSES IN THE UK
BA (Hons) Dance and Drama – University of Lincoln
www.qurl.com/linchor
BA (Hons) Dance Making and Performance – Coventry University
www.qurl.com/covchor
BA (Hons) Dance – Kingston University
www.qurl.com/kingchor
BA (Hons) Dance Performance – Middlesex University
www.qurl.com/mdxchor
BA (Hons) Dance Theatre – Plymouth University
www.qurl.com/plychor
BA (Hons) Dance Theatre – Trinity Laban
www.qurl.com/trinchor

Fight Director

The Fight Director choreographs fight scenes for the stage in a certain style or from a certain era. They may work alongside the Director or Choreographer.

USEFUL ORGANISATIONS
The British Academy of Stage & Screen Combat – **www.bassc.org**
The British Academy of Dramatic Conflict – **www.badc.co.uk**

FIGHT DIRECTING COURSES IN THE UK
Fighting For Film – City Literary Institute
www.qurl.com/cityfight

Producer

The Producer oversees many aspects of the production, and often acts as the point of contact for sponsors or investors interested in the production. They may be responsible for marketing, attend rehearsals, meet with the production team, and deal with problems as they occur.

© ALEXANDER PARSONAGE

Stage Jobs Pro member Flavia Fraser-Cannon is a Producer. We asked her the following questions about her career:

What is the most rewarding aspect of working as a Producer?

Standing outside the theatre when the show comes down and seeing an audience fired up about it. The buzz of a satisfied and engaged audience is thrilling.

What are the key skills required to be an effective Producer?

Time management, a strong sense of responsibilty, determination, trust, empathy, strength, good judgement and a head for figures (or a good spreadsheet/calculator).

Do you see your role as a natural step on a career ladder, and if so what is the next rung?

The next rung for me I think would be moving towards becoming an executive director. Slightly different skill set but still people and money management. You can of course be a producer for life though, and plenty of people do. It's such a varied career that there's plenty to keep you on your toes!

How did you work your way into your current role?

I have had experience in almost all areas of theatre from front of house, duty management and box office to stage management, acting, helping with costumes and teching and even a couple of times directing. I think the better you can understand the various roles that you are interacting with the better you can manage all the aspects of a production, talk on a level with people etc. Then again a more money based producer could come directly from all sorts of areas of business.

How much do you think networking helps towards landing a job in the industry?

A great deal, as with all industries. You will move forward quicker if people see you around, get to know you personally and find you personable. People are always more inclined to work with someone they know. Plus if people see you around you are keeping yourself fresh in their minds when they are looking for someone like you.

Do you think you will be working in the industry in the next five years, and if so in what capacity?

Same capacity, moving more into touring rather than being rooted in London and the Edinburgh festival – longer runs are more financially sustainable and regional venues have a more producer friendly guarantees model.

Please describe what a typical day working as a Producer might contain?

EVERYTHING! But really, sifting through the morning emails, making a list of things that need to be addressed from contracts to distributing schedules, liaising with marketing, press, tech etc, keeping an eye on the budgets and cash flow, paying invoices and sending invoices out. And then getting on with all those things! Then probably seeing a show in the evening.

Have you done any additional training courses to further your career?

Stage One are great for starting out commercial producers. They run a short course once a year and offer various schemes for work placements, bursaries and investment in start out projects. Otherwise, I believe there are some MA courses now, I don't know a great deal about them though if I'm honest. Just go out and get some experience, intern with a bigger producer and start producing small projects to begin with and build up.

How important is working for free at the beginning of your career?

If I put all the time I worked for free back to back I'd probably spent about 2 years at it! But it was spread out over a few years and I would get paid stuff in between. The industry as it stands needs people to do work placements to survive and continuing arts cuts will not help this issue. Interning does also offer the fantastic opportunity to learn from observation, you can avoid making a few nasty little starting out mistakes by doing this. I still help friends out here and there for free even now, as a goodwill gesture. You never know when you might need to ask for a favour back.

Flavia is the in-house producer at Theatre503: **www.theatre503.com**

PRODUCING COURSES IN THE UK
The Role of the Producer/General Manager (9 weeks) – RADA
www.qurl.com/radaprod
MA/MFA Creative Producing – CSSD
www.qurl.com/cssdprod
MA Creative Producing – Birbeck
www.qurl.com/bbkprod

Production Manager

The Production Manager is concerned with practical and administrative aspects of a production: overseeing technical aspects, schedule and budget. They must be excellent at planning and problem-solving, good with numbers and liaise with the various departments. Production Managers tend to move on to bigger productions and work for larger venues as they develop their skills and experience.

PRODUCTION MANAGER COURSES IN THE UK
One year Theatre Production Management (PG Dip) – Bristol Old Vic
www.qurl.com/oldvicpm

Tour Manager

Tour Managers are responsible for the practical aspects of touring – controlling finances, booking accommodation, preparing schedules, and communicating with theatres. They must be very good at budgeting and communicating, and have excellent organisational abilities, as well as the ability to respond to any complaints or queries from the cast.

Writer

The Writer creates theatrical pieces for the stage. They often come from a creative writing background, and, depending on the scale of the production that they are writing for, may have to develop the script with the Director.

If you fancy yourself as a bit of a scribe, Andrew Loretto wrote this great article for Get Into Theatre on getting your work out there:

How do I get my play read?

THIS ARTICLE HAS BEEN REPRODUCED IN ITS ENTIRETY WITH KIND PERMISSION FROM GET INTO THEATRE
AUTHOR: ANDREW LORETTO, CO-DIRECTOR, CHOL THEATRE, HUDDERSFIELD

T he people who you need to target are literary managers and directors of new writing. If they like the work, and see your potential, then you'll hopefully get your foot on the development and commissioning ladder.

getintotheatre

Don't send out work in a blanket fashion. Which theatres you should send your work to depends on the type of plays you have written. Check out the new writing venues and organisations local to your region in the first instance. Look at their websites first to see if they commission the type of work you are writing.

Policy

Most producing theatres have their new writing and submissions policy on the website. Look at the mix of work they develop and stage. For example, some companies are interested in plays for young people, others not. Some venues have a preference for more naturalistic, linear narrative forms, and others will steer away from narrative, preferring to use words in a more experimental fashion. And some companies don't develop traditional playwrights as such but take a very broad view of writing eg the writer as performance poet or MC.

Companies

There are many venues and companies interested in new writing. There are also new writing agencies and support structures around the UK – such as Script Yorkshire. These are of course just some of the key new writing venues and producers. There are many smaller companies and fringe-based organisations offering opportunities for new writing to be developed and staged.

Festivals

There are also some excellent new writing festivals around with open submissions policies such as High Tide and 24:7. Again, check out websites, find out about their policies for new writing.

Listings

Read The List, Leeds Guide, Time Out magazine – whatever listings guide is local to your area – see where work is being staged and then go and see it if you're interested.

Put yourself on free mail and email newsletter lists – including Artsnews and Artsjobs (sign up via Arts Council England main website). A really useful resource for screen/radio new writing is the BBC Writersroom website.

> **"The people who you need to target are literary managers and directors of new writing"**

Agent

In terms of getting an agent as a writer, that tends to happen once you've had a play staged or promoted by a reasonably high-profile theatre company or as part of a festival. If your work has been seen by the agent and they like it enough, they might take you on.

If and when you have any work staged – either fully or as part of a 'work in progress' type of event – do your utmost to get people along to see it. As with approaching the venues, choose the agent carefully according to the type of work (and level of writer) they are interested in representing.

Have a look at who their other clients are – that usually gives you a clue as to what kind of work they're into.

Groups

Writers' groups are useful if they operate at a level that challenges and stimulates you creatively. If you feel you are going over old ground, then it can actually be counter-productive. If you're checking out a writers' group, do a little research into who's leading it, who else is currently in the group, and what kind of work they're doing at the moment. You might be able to take part in one or two sessions on a trial basis. One thing I would always caution against is paying money up front for a whole series of writers' sessions – especially when the larger theatres offer free and low-cost training options.

Good luck!

This article has been reproduced in its entirety with kind permission from Get Into Theatre. Their site hopes to open your eyes to the huge variety of careers in the industry – and the different ways to get there. You can find out more at **www.getintotheatre.com**.

BOOKS ON WRITING FOR THE THEATRE
So You Want to Be a Playwright?: How to Write a Play and Get it Produced, Tim Fountain, 2007
The Playwright's Guidebook, Stuart Spencer, 2003
The Crafty Art of Playmaking, Alan Ayckbourn, 2007

THEATRE WRITING COURSES IN THE UK
MA Writing for Stage and Broadcast Media – Central School of Speech and Drama
www.qurl.com/cssdwrite
MRes Playwriting Studies – University of Birmingham
www.qurl.com/birwrite
BA (Hons) Scriptwriting and Performance – University of East Anglia
www.qurl.com/ueawrite
BA (Hons) Drama and Creative Writing – Liverpool John Moores University
www.qurl.com/ljmuwrite
BA (Hons) Drama and Creative Professional Writing – University of Wolverhampton
www.qurl.com/wlvwrite
BA (Hons) Theatre and Creative Writing – Brunel University
www.qurl.com/bwrite
MA Creative Writing – Southampton Solent University
www.qurl.com/swrite
MA Creative Writing – Birkbeck College, University of London
www.qurl.com/brikwrite
MA Creative Writing – Loughborough University
www.qurl.com/lborowrite

Front of House, Marketing & Theatre Administration

Working in Theatre Management, Administration and Marketing is a rewarding career path and ideal if you're perhaps less interested in the technical or practical backstage paths. If you work in a receiving theatre there will be a constant stream of incoming and outgoing productions, the logistics of which require an immense amount of planning and a very particular skillset. If you work for a producing theatre you'll get to experience the full circle of theatre production – from development and marketing through to the final production.

We've listed the most common roles for working in this environment, with some interesting case studies from Stage Jobs Pro members who are working in this area of theatre.

Administration

Admin Assistant
Admin Assistants are responsible for general day-to-day administrative tasks, ensuring that the production, theatre or venue runs smoothly. They take care of administrative tasks that might otherwise occupy the time of the rest of the company – this can include paperwork, dealing with emails, answering the telephone, organising meetings and events, and managing diaries. Admin Assistants must have excellent organisational skills, and be very efficient. Admin Assistants might report to the Theatre Manager, Box Office Manager, General Manager or Administrative Director. Admin Assistants may progress to the position of Theatre Administrator.

Theatre Administrator
Theatre Administrators allow other members of staff to tackle their jobs by completing vital, but often time-consuming, tasks. Administrators must be excellent communicators and very good at multi-tasking. In a normal day, they might have to deal with paperwork, communicating with theatre companies, and a myriad of other concerns required to keep things running smoothly and efficiently. Administrators might report to the Theatre Manager,

General Manager or Administrative Director. Theatre Administrators can progress to being Administrative Director, Production Manager and Events Manager or Theatre Manager.

General Manager

The General Manager oversees administrative and financial matters, liaises between departments, and may act as the Human Resources manager. They are expected to deal with any problems that may arise. The General Manager may move on to work as Theatre / Venue Manager.

Theatre/Venue Manager

The role of Theatre/Venue Manager encompasses a huge variety of obligations – the Theatre Manager may be responsible for human resources management, customer services, health and safety, and financial management. Theatre Managers must be excellent communicators, great at multi-tasking and good at problem-solving. Theatre Managers have often previously worked in a variety of theatre roles, such as Front of House Manager or General Manager, and so will have a thorough understanding of the theatre industry. Theatre Managers may move on to become Administrative Director or Artistic Director.

Stage Jobs Pro member Mel Dixon is a Theatre Manager. We asked her the following questions about her career:

What is the most rewarding aspect of working as a Theatre / Venue Manager?
Being happy that everything and everyone is running smoothly.

What are the key skills required to be an effective Theatre / Venue Manager?
The ability to prioritise and multi-task. The ability to work under extreme pressure and stay calm.

Flexibility – you need to switch priorities at a moments notice. The ability to balance budgets, utilise every bit of knowledge, scrap of information to its best advantage. The ability to spot and maximise on any potential. The ability to understand, organise and adhere to legislative requirements The ability to manage staff. The ability to manage budgets. The ability to negotiate, project manage, schedule, write concise reports. The ability to adapt in any and all directions.

Do you see your role as a natural step on a career ladder, and if so what is the next rung?
As I would like to freelance and only do short interim cover I have to answer no. My target is to obtain work in any theatre-based role while I develop my own projects. I prefer breezing in and out to full-time employment, enjoy doing lots of different things and utilising that to resolve problems in a wide variety of roles. I enjoy alternating between leading and following and dislike being in either position for any great length of time.

How did you work your way into your current role?
I finished my last contract and started looking for freelance opportunities.

How much do you think networking helps towards landing a job in the industry?
Totally indispensable.

Do you think you will be working in the industry in the next five years, and if so in what capacity?
Yes – I'd be miserable if I wasn't. Workshop practitioner (freelance), Emergency Managerial cover (short interim cover), Casual/freelance technician (lighting) and stage crew/ds, Freelance LD Project Co-ordinator/Manager, Writer and possibly producer or director.

Please describe what a typical day working as a Theatre / Venue Manager might contain.
There's no such thing as a typical day! However... You could be dealing with: Hire enquiries, Contracts, Licensing, Invoicing, Staffing, Maintenance, Interviews, Budgeting, Credit Control Reports and analysis, Marketing Operations, Company, or Board Meetings, Repairs, Facilities, Development of Facilities, Staff training and development, H&S Inspections, Fire Risk Assessments, Licensing agreements, PRS, Insurance and CRBs, Co-ordinating logistics for festivals or events, Greeting or assisting with a get in, Rolling up your sleeves to help cafe, FOH, technical or any other staff who are up against it. The list is endless...

Have you done any additional training courses to further your career?
Not really. I'd like to have but either I've been too busy working or I haven't had the money to spare. I learn on the job mainly.

How important is working for free at the beginning of your career?
A good idea generally and also volunteering throughout your career can give you experience that might not otherwise be available when you need it.

ARTS MANAGEMENT COURSES IN THE **UK**

BA (Hons) Music, Theatre, and Entertainment Management – Liverpool Institute of Performing Arts

www.qurl.com/lipaman

MA Cultural Management – Queen Margaret University

www.qurl.com/qmuman

MA Cultural and Arts Management – University of Winchester

www.qurl.com/winman

PG Dip Theatre Arts Management – Bristol Old Vic Theatre School

www.qurl.com/oldvicman

Artistic Director

The Artistic Director is responsible for managing the creative aspects of a theatre or production company, often working with a Chief Executive. They may have to organise and manage fundraising, develop the creative policies of the theatre, and organise the programming. It's the Artistic Director's remit to shape the ethos of a theatre company and decide what they're going to commission or schedule. Artistic Directors usually have a wide range of theatre experience, and so have a thorough and wide-ranging understanding of theatre as well as a variety of creative skills.

Stage Door Keeper

The Stage Door Keeper looks after the Stage Door, ensuring that it is secure and preventing unauthorised members of the public from entering the backstage area. They may also be charged with looking after dressing room keys, registering who is in the building, and acting as the point of contact for deliveries.

Marketing

Press & Marketing Assistant

The Press & Marketing Assistant works with the Press & Marketing Manager to plan, develop, and run marketing campaigns to advertise a production or venue. Normal career progression is to Press & Marketing Manager or Producer.

Press & Marketing Manager

The Press & Marketing Manager plans, develops, and runs marketing campaigns to advertise a production or venue. They must have excellent analytical skills, in order to be able to look at financial statistics and assess marketing techniques. Another important part of the role of Press & Marketing Manager is networking, so the Press & Marketing Manager must be very good at communicating and working with people. The Press & Marketing Manager may be aided by a Press & Marketing Assistant.

USEFUL ORGANISATIONS

The Arts Marketing Association – www.a-m-a.org.uk

Front of House

Usher

Ushering is often the first job for people starting their theatre careers, as it gives a good grounding in front of house and production duties. Ushers are the public face of a theatre, and must be able to help audience members and answer any queries they may have, as well as checking tickets and selling programmes and merchandise.

Front of House Manager

The Front of House Manager manages customer service at a venue, making sure that the Ushers and Front of House staff are working to a high standard. They liaise with the Company Manager, make sure that important information is known to both the theatre and the touring company, and also deal with audience complaints or problems on the night. At other times, the Front of House Manager completes administrative tasks and compiles staff rotas.

119

Box Office

Box Office Assistant
The Box Office Assistant works in the box office selling tickets to the public and answering customer queries face-to-face, over the telephone or online. Box Office Assistants may go on to work as Box Office Managers.

Box Office Manager
The Box Office Manager is responsible for managing ticket sales, and is the line manager for the Box Office Assistants and Box Office Assistant Manager. They create staff rotas, analyse ticket sales, write sales reports, work out marketing strategies for poor-selling shows (often with the Press & Marketing Officer) and attend staff meetings.

Events Manager
The Events Manager plans and manages events, so must have a thorough working knowledge of Health & Safety, excellent time management skills, be good at managing people, and possess great attention to detail. They may work freelance or work for a theatre or company, and may previously have worked as Stage Managers or Production Managers.

Fundraising/Development

Development Manager
The Development Manager is responsible for raising money for the theatre or theatre company. They identify sources of funding, create fundraising strategies, and run funding drives. They must be good at networking and engaging with people.

Audience Development Officer
The Audience Development Officer is charged with attracting more people, or a more diverse audience, to a theatre. They plan, develop, and implement marketing campaigns, and so creativity and an understanding of marketing is very useful. Audience Development Officers may have previously worked as a Press & Marketing Officer.

Chapter 2
Training

Training

If you're considering a career in theatre the best thing to do is get busy – work on your school productions, speak to local am dram groups and professional theatres and see if you can help out to start getting vital experience. Doing so also helps to give you a grounding in the different areas of theatre so you can start exploring to find your particular areas of interest – you will have seen from the Case Studies in the previous chapter that lots of people fall into their specialism almost by accident! Watch lots of theatre and read books – educate yourself as much as possible about what's out there. Chapters 1 and 3 of this Handbook will help you out with suggestions for further reading and websites.

Something that's definitely worth subscribing to is 'The Stage': the weekly newspaper for the performing arts industry which will keep you up to date with the latest news and developments in theatre . Each union and organisation will have its own email newsletter with important news and information which you can sign up to receive. Check Chapter 3, 'Key Organisations', for suggestions.

You could also check out TheatreCraft which is a free careers event in London for anyone aged 17 to 25 looking for a non-performance career in theatre. You can find out more at **www.theatrecraft.org**.

The following are the main training pathways into the theatre industry – it's worth keeping your mind open to the route that works best for you.

Pathways to a career in theatre

Further Education & College

Age: Usually 16-18
Stage of education: Completed compulsory school education
Qualification: A-level, BTEC, IB, Cambridge Pre-U, or NVQ
Institution: School or Sixth Form College

Further Education takes place after the age of 16, in your last two years of school, or over two years at a college. Most students get the choice to drop some subjects, and focus on others, although the extent to which this occurs depends on the qualification you are working towards. Having an FE qualification can allow you to then go on and study for a Higher Education qualification, but also allows you to study for practical and vocational BTECs. There are a wide variety of further education subjects, and each further education institution will only teach a few, so you may have to search through a few college and sixth form prospectuses to find somewhere that teaches the subjects you want to take, ideally with a theatre focus.

DirectGov has more information at **www.qurl.com/dgovfe**

Higher Education

Age: Usually 18+
Stage of education: Finished secondary school / graduated 6th form college / completed college education
Qualification: Foundation Degree, BA, BSc, Diploma, MA, MFA, MSc, or other.
Institution: University, College, Conservatoire, or Drama School

Higher Education courses come in many forms depending on the subject you're interested in, the institution and the level at which you're studying – you can take anything from a Foundation Degree to a PhD. The subjects you can study are also a lot more diverse at a higher education level, with a much wider variety than at GCSE, A-level, Highers, or similar qualifications.

Whether you choose to study at a higher education institution depends on a variety of factors – financial, personal, and which career path you're interested in. There's no question that a degree from a good course or drama school with strong vocational and practical content, and direct links to the industry can seriously improve your chances of employment after graduation.

DirectGov has information on getting into Higher Education at **www.qurl.com/dgovhe**

When and How to Choose Your Course

THIS GUIDE WAS KINDLY WRITTEN BY ROBIN TOWNLEY, ASSOCIATE EXECUTIVE OFFICER AT THE ASSOCIATION OF BRITISH THEATRE TECHNICIANS

The purpose of this section is to help you decide when and how it would be best for you to choose a course. Choosing a suitable course to provide you with some of the tools you will need to pursue a career behind the scenes is always a very important decision. You will always be in a position whereby you will be investing a great deal in the process. You will be committing to invest your time, your energy and your money, not only to pay for tuition and examination or assessment fees, but also in living and travel expenses. You will want to be confident that your investment is worthwhile and that it will achieve the goals you have set yourself. To help you achieve this you must always think about what it is that you really need to do next to prepare you for work or allow you to progress in your career. When you have identified exactly what you need to do to reach your goal you must analyse carefully the next step or steps you need to take to get there.

To undertake any job you need to be competent at the tasks that job requires. Competence is the ability to undertake responsibilities and to perform tasks to a recognised standard on a regular basis. Competence is always a combination of three fundamental ingredients:

• Skill,

• Knowledge and

• Experience.

When thinking about how to choose the best way to prepare yourself for any kind of job it is always sensible to consider not only how you will gain the necessary knowledge you will need for the work but also how you will gain the skills you will need and how and where you will find opportunities to develop the necessary experience that you will require.

Very often you will decide that in order to most effectively gain the next area of knowledge that you have identified you need for your career it would be best to gain some related experience first.

When thinking about how to prepare for a career and how to go about choosing a course it is always a good idea to identify what you need in

"In order to understand exactly what a course is designed to provide it is always best to talk to advisors or teaching staff involved"

terms of Skill, Knowledge and Experience. You can do this by talking to people who already work in the industry or to advisors and teaching staff involved in running related training and courses of education.

When choosing a course remember that not all courses are designed to achieve the same thing and that different types of course will be more appropriate for your own needs at different points in your education and career.

In order to understand exactly what a course is designed to provide it is always best to talk to advisors or teaching staff involved in delivering the course itself. However, it is useful to think about four general types of courses when you start your discussions:

- Educational Courses with a vocational context
- Vocational Courses
- Educational Courses in Preparation for a Vocational Career
- Career Development Courses

Educational Courses with a vocational context

This type of course is designed to continue the delivery of a general educational syllabus but using the context of a particular industry or career to provide a basis for learning. These courses are a very useful way of continuing general education while beginning to gain foundation knowledge in a particular career area.

Vocational Courses

These courses are specifically designed to provide students with the knowledge they require for a particular job. They also provide opportunities for skills to be obtained and for participants to begin to gain the experience they require to gain competence in their chosen career. These courses are often a very good way of obtaining sufficient competence to commence professional work in a particular job.

Educational Course in Preparation for a Vocational Career

This type of course is very often a higher education course leading to a degree in a particular vocational subject. The course will develop academic skills as well as providing for the acquisition of vocational knowledge and perhaps some skills and experience.

Career Development Courses

These courses very often provide specific training in particular equipment or techniques. They may be short courses and they are often designed to be taken as part of on-going career development.

As a general point all courses tend to include good opportunities to achieve new knowledge. Some, but not all, provide opportunities for developing and practising new skills both mental and physical. The hardest element for a course to provide is experience.

It is also worth remembering that it is very often the case that it is much easier to absorb new knowledge and indeed gain much more benefit from a knowledge based course if you have had some experience beforehand. It is certainly true that you will find studying on a course related to working backstage much more beneficial and interesting if you have already had the opportunity to become familiar with the working environment behind the scenes.

Working behind the scenes is very interesting and challenging and can provide a huge amount of satisfaction. However, it is never possible to predict what knowledge, skills or experience will be useful in solving the next problem with which you will be presented. In planning a training path towards working backstage it is always worth continuing a broad education as long as possible while pursuing opportunities to gain experience in the working environment whenever possible.

Such experience can be gained through the support of performances at school, college and university. There are many local, community, amateur and professional companies who will give interested volunteers the opportunity to gain experience working on the presentation and support of performance. There are opportunities for part-time employment in many theatres and venues through which experience can be gained while still pursuing general education.

Of the four types of course discussed above the first three very often represent the last opportunity within your working career through which you are able to continue learning and pursue the acquisition of knowledge on a full-time basis. After the completion of these courses the fact that you will wish to start working in the industry means that you will have to pursue further learning at the same time as being employed. Such courses very often provide you with the biggest single component of your professional knowledge and will be the basis on which you found your career.

In conclusion here is a brief checklist which you will find helpful when considering when and how to choose a course:

- Seek to pursue a broad education when it is available while gaining experience behind the scenes wherever and whenever possible.
- Always identify what your learning requirements are and what the balance is between skill, knowledge and experience.
- Remember that some prior experience is very useful in making the most of opportunities to gain further knowledge and skills.
- Identify your learning aims and make sure you understand what steps you need to take to achieve them.
- Always discuss your needs and the content and strengths of courses with the appropriate advisors before making any decisions.
- Remember that you will continue to gain new skills, knowledge and experience throughout your career and that this can be one of the most rewarding aspects of your working experience.

Robin Townley is the Associate Executive Officer at the Association of British Theatre Technicians. You can find out more about The ABTT at **www.abtt.org.uk**.

Apprenticeships

Age: Must be 16 or over
Qualification: Varies – often NVQ, but depends on the apprenticeship.

Anyone who has left school and who is not in full time education is eligible for an apprenticeship. The main advantage of an apprenticeship is that you learn, studying and earning a qualification, at the same time as earning money. This is different from studying part-time and working, because, as an apprentice, your studies are related to your work, and your work is designed not only to be useful to your employer, but also to teach you specific skills and learning outcomes. Apprentices are paid a low wage – the national minimum wage for apprentices is £2.65 an hour – and are allowed at least 20 days paid holiday a year.

Apprenticeships are vocational – they lead into a specific career path. If you know exactly what you want to do, and want to get started immediately, this could be the best option.

What are Apprenticeships?

THIS GUIDE WAS KINDLY WRITTEN BY ROBERT WEST, DIRECTOR OF PROGRAMMES AT CREATIVE & CULTURAL SKILLS

A pprenticeships are becoming a great way to break into the arts. Targeted at people over 16 years old who are non-graduates and not in full-time education, Creative Apprenticeships were set up to provide an alternative route into creative industries, including theatre. Apprentices get on-the-job training, whilst studying for a qualification and earning at the same time.

As employees, apprentices earn a wage and work alongside experienced staff to gain job-specific skills. Off the job, apprentices receive training to work towards nationally recognised qualifications, and there are now various Apprenticeship qualification pathways to follow such as: Live events and promotion, Music Business, Technical Theatre, Costume & Wardrobe, Venue Operations, Design and Community Arts.

There are three levels of Apprenticeship available: Intermediate Level Apprenticeships, Advanced Level Apprenticeships, and Higher Apprenticeships, and an Apprentice can work their way through these levels. Apprentices are employed for the length of time it takes to complete all the qualifications within the Apprenticeship, and each level usually lasts somewhere between nine and eighteen months.

"*Apprentices get on-the-job training, whilst studying for a qualification and earning at the same time*"

For an arts organisation Apprenticeships mean they can develop their workforce for the future teaching good practice, values and beliefs from the moment the apprentice joins the company. In turn an apprentice can also help organisations gain a better appreciation of a younger and more local audience.

Creative & Cultural Skills have case studies available from apprentices who have successfully completed, or are in the middle of an apprenticeship (**www.nsa-ccskills.co.uk/apprentices-success-stories**), whilst a Facebook group has been set up by some Creative

Apprentices themselves offering a self run support network (**www.facebook.com/groups/135411059928851**).

All Apprenticeship vacancies can be found on the National Apprenticeship website **www.apprenticeships.org.uk**. The National Skills Academy for Creative & Cultural list specific vacancies in theatre on their popular website **getintotheatre.org**.

The Skills Academy is a membership network of 20 colleges and over 225 theatre and live music employers nationwide. The Skills Academy recognise, develop and improve skills opportunities to help people get into the industry and get on in it once you're there. For more information visit **www.nsa-ccskills.org.uk**

Robert West is the Director of Programmes at Creative & Cultural Skills. Creative & Cultural Skills is the licensed Sector Skills Council for the UK's creative and cultural industries, including craft, cultural heritage, design, literature, music, performing arts and visual arts and you can find out more at **www.ccskills.org.uk**

Internships, Work Experience & Other Options

Internships and work experience tend to be unpaid though you may get expenses to cover your living costs. Internships and work experience are great as a route into the industry, as you can make contacts, get experience, gain referees, and learn about specific aspects of theatre. Do make sure that your internship includes specific learning outcomes, the chance to work and learn from professionals and feedback on how you're doing to ensure you get the best from your time. Depending on the company or organisation you're working for, doing an internship can sometimes lead to a job. If you decide to study theatre at college or university, your department may help to organise a work placement as part of your course.

And lastly, many HE institutions, drama schools and independent course providers also run specialised short courses (such as RADA's 1 week Property Making for the Stage course) which usually require less investment of time and money. These courses are designed for someone who's interested in a particular field of work, but is not ready to commit to a long-term course. We've included some examples of short courses in Chapter 1, but take the time to research what courses are available in your area.

Funding your Training

Due to recent changes in the UK university fee system, studying for a higher education qualification has, in many institutions, become significantly more expensive with standard course fees costing as much as £9,000 per year. In addition to this, students will still have to pay for accommodation, travel, any necessary course materials, and living expenses. These costs will vary depending on the location of the course – for example, rent and living costs are considerably more expensive in London than in other regions. Furthermore, a well-paid contract is by no means guaranteed upon graduation and developing a career in theatre can take a very long time, often involving working for free and investing significant amounts of money in finding out about jobs through The Stage, Stage Jobs Pro and other services, as well as paying for membership of relevant associations.

Nonetheless, the benefits of having a higher education qualification often justify the costs, providing career opportunities, valuable theatre contacts, and giving theatre professionals a strong advantage when applying for jobs.

Do remember, however, that while a university education can be very expensive, the cost need not be prohibitive. Student Loans can cover the cost of both the training and living costs.

MoneySavingExpert.com has a very useful guide to student finance and student loans at **www.moneysavingexpert.com/students**.

Student Loans

Student Loans are available to UK and EU students in full-time or part-time higher education. There are two types of student loan – tuition fee loans, and maintenance loans. Student Loans are determined by your financial background, and are indexed to the rate of inflation. The Student Finance Calculator on **www.direct.gov.uk** can be used to calculate the loans, grants, and bursaries for which you are eligible. MoneySavingExpert.com also has a comprehensive introduction to student loans at **www.qurl.com/students**

132

Tuition Fee Loans

The Tuition Fee Loan covers course fees in full, and is paid directly to the university or college. Because of the changes in the university fee system, Tuition Fee Loans will increase to a maximum of £9000 to cover the increase in tuition fees. The size of the loan is dependent on whether the course is full-time or part-time, and whether the university or college is private. Tuition Fee Loans are lower for private universities and colleges – the maximum private tuition loan is £6000. Tuition fee loans do not have to be paid back until you have graduated and your income is over £15,795 pa.

Maintenance Loans

Maintenance Loans help to cover living costs, such as the cost of accommodation, food, travel, and course materials.

Maintenance Loans are only available to students in full-time higher education. Eligible students are automatically entitled to 65% of the maximum maintenance loan, which is dependent on where they are living – at home, away from home in London, away from home outside of London – and which year of study they are in. This percentage is unaffected by household income but the remainder of the loan is dependent on an assessment of the income of both student and household income.

Students with a household income of less than £42,600 can also get a maintenance grant – money for maintenance that does not have to be repaid. This is in addition to the maintenance loan, and so should ensure that students from all economic backgrounds can pay for day-to-day costs while at university.

A warning: whilst Maintenance Loans do cover living costs, many students have been known to get excited by having a large amount of money in their bank account and spend it all very quickly, meaning that they are then forced to spend the rest of the term living on a shoestring. Budgeting at university is very important, and there are lots of resources online to help you with this.

For up-to-date details on student loans, check the DirectGov student loans webpages, **www.qurl.com/finance** and **www.qurl.com/unifunds**

Bursaries and Scholarships

Many universities and colleges have bursary and scholarship schemes. These vary from institution to institution, ranging from full course fees and help towards living expenses, to smaller amounts which will only cover some of your costs. Bursaries are usually dependent on your household income – the amount of money earned by the people in your home.

There will only be a limited number of bursaries and scholarships given out each year, and a lot of competition for them, so they can not be relied on as sources of funding. Each establishment will have different scholarships and bursaries, so it is very important to check the details thoroughly before applying. For a full list of the scholarships offered by universities go to **www.scholarship-search.org.uk**

Various organisations and schemes, such as The Standing Conference of University Drama Departments, BBC Performing Arts Fund and Dance and Drama Awards also provide bursaries and scholarships to theatre students.

Useful websites
Conference of University Drama Departments
www.scudd.org.uk
Scholarship Search
www.scholarship-search.org.uk
BBC Performing Arts Fund
www.bbc.co.uk/performingartsfund
Dance and Drama Awards
www.qurl.com/dadas

Charities and other sources

It is also possible to raise funds from charities, trusts, and foundations. If you are going down this route, make sure you target suitable sources of funding carefully and avoid simply sending out a standard letter to lots of organisations. Your application is much more likely to be successful if you've written to organisations which have some reason to be interested in funding you, and if you then tailor your letter specifically to them, rather than sending out a standard letter to lots of organisations. Another route might be to approach local businesses who have shown evidence of supporting the arts – check out local newspapers and theatres to see which sponsors' logos appear and make contact with them.

When raising funds to pay for courses, it is also possible to get sponsorship from local authorities and individuals, but once again, it is important to approach individuals who are likely to be interested in supporting someone in theatre training, and to approach them with a specific letter or call, rather than just sending the same email to as many people as possible.

Keep your options open

For many stage jobs, higher education training is not strictly necessary (see Simon Lovelace's guide to crewing for more on this in Chapter 1) and, particularly for practical roles, it is often possible to build your career through working and networking. Practical experience and good references can be as useful as higher education qualifications. Enthusiasm can get you a long way if you get involved in everything – do tech for school productions, help out with local amateur dramatics groups, or volunteer to do the light and sound for a school fashion show or performance. Doing this will mean that you have experience and references, which can then help you to progress.

Studying part-time while working can also be a more feasible option than attending university full-time, and then having to deal with the costs.

Some people decide to study full-time and work during term-time (as well as during the holidays), but it is important to remember that the main point of going to university or college is to study. If your work schedule means that you are compromising on study, it may be better to stop working, study effectively, and then potentially spend slightly longer repaying loans.

FUNDING: USEFUL LINKS & ORGANISATIONS

Direct Gov – Student Finance

www.qurl.com/unifunds

The Student Loans Company

www.slc.co.uk

Direct Gov – Dance and Drama Awards

www.direct.gov.uk/DanceandDrama

Student Finance Wales

www.studentfinancewales.co.uk

Student Awards Agency for Scotland

www.saas.gov.uk

Student Finance Northern Ireland

www.studentfinanceni.co.uk

National Council for Drama Training guide to funding

www.ncdt.co.uk/guidetotraining/funding

Prospects – funding my further study

www.prospects.ac.uk/funding_my_further_study.htm

Direct Gov – Professional and Career Development Loans

www.qurl.com/cdloans

Skillset – Key funding and development bodies

www.creativeskillset.org/funding/alternative_funding

Money Saving Expert: Students & Financial Education

www.moneysavingexpert.com/students

NUS – Money and Funding

www.nus.org.uk/cy/advice/money-and-funding/higher-education

Student Cash Point – finding grants, loans, and other ways of sponsoring your higher education

www.studentcashpoint.co.uk

A-Z of Colleges & Universities

There is such a large number of colleges and institutions offering theatre courses across the UK that it's really worth taking the time to do your research and find out which one is best for you: what does the course focus on? Does it include placements? What have students gone on to do? Does it start out broad and give you a chance to specialise in the final year? What are the facilities like? How much does it cost – and would you have to leave home and pay for uni digs too? What is the town or city like? Remember you'll be spending a few years there so it's important you like the place!

To help you make a start, we've made an A-Z of the most commonly attended institutions by Stage Jobs Pro members – and included testimonials about their time there.

Drama UK

Drama UK (formerly the National Council of Drama Training and the Conference of Drama Schools) accredits drama training courses which it feels offer the highest levels of vocational training, and offers information on drama training. Panels of industry professionals regularly inspect courses and grant official accreditation to those which they consider offer a high level of professional relevance. You can see a list of accredited courses at **www.dramauk.co.uk**.

Do keep in mind, however, that there are plenty of schools which run well regarded courses that don't have Drama UK accreditation.

A-Z of Course Providers in the UK

The following is a list of some of the most commonly attended HE institutions by members of Stage Jobs Pro. The list is by no means exhaustive and there is more information on course providers at **www.stagejobspro.com/uk/colleges.php**.

We've also included the number of SJP members who have attended these institutions. These figures are correct at the time of going to press.

ABERYSTWYTH UNIVERSITY
OLD COLLEGE, KING STREET
ABERYSTWYTH, SY23 2AX
TEL: 01970 623 111
TFTS@ABER.AC.UK
WWW.ABER.AC.UK
SJP MEMBERS: **223**
COURSES: BA (HONS) DRAMA AND THEATRE STUDIES, 3 YEARS; BA (HONS) SCENOGRAPHY & THEATRE DESIGN, 3 YEARS
DEADLINE: 15TH JANUARY
The Department of Theatre, Film and Television Studies is one of the largest in Britain in terms of both staff and student numbers. It has some outstanding facilities and is committed to offering you an integrated scheme of study, combining a wide range of practice-based work with challenging academic activity. The Department offers some of the most exciting, radical and popular Higher Education courses available today. There has been a revolution in these disciplines during the past twenty years, and this department has led the way in asserting the value and vitality of creative studies underpinned by a strong emphasis on the relationship between theory and practice.

ALRA (ACADEMY OF LIVE AND RECORDED ARTS)
STUDIO 24, ROYAL VICTORIA PATRIOTIC BUILDING
JOHN ARCHER WAY,
LONDON SW18 3SX
TEL: 020 8870 6475
INFO@ALRA.CO.UK
WWW.ALRA.CO.UK
SJP MEMBERS: **176**
COURSES: TECHNICAL PRODUCTION FOR LIVE & RECORDED ARTS , 1 YEAR, (15 STUDENTS)
STAGE MANAGEMENT & TECHNICAL THEATRE FOUNDATION DEGREE, 2 YEARS, (15 STUDENTS)
DEADLINE: 15TH JANUARY
ALRA aims to equip actors and theatre technicians with those skills fundamental to a productive and creative life in the performance industries. ALRA is dedicated to helping students of all backgrounds and ages to enter the world of live and recorded arts. ALRA has a distinguished record of producing professionals prepared and ready to work. ALRA is the only CDS drama school to offer a combined theatre and television training throughout the programme – starting in week one. Technicians have the opportunity to work in both live

theatre and the recording studios. All our tutors staff have connections and experience with the theatre and TV industries; Directors of final productions are all professional directors with a current CV; contact time is at least 35 hours a week; our ideal group size is 14 and best of all, your work will be seen in two major theatre centres – London and the Northwest.

ARTS UNIVERSITY COLLEGE BOURNEMOUTH
WALLISDOWN, POOLE
DORSET BH12 5HH
TEL: 01202 533 011
GENERAL@AUCB.AC.UK
WWW.AUCB.AC.UK
SJP MEMBERS: **264**
COURSES: BA (HONS) MAKE-UP FOR MEDIA & PERFORMANCE, 3 YEARS
BA (HONS) COSTUME WITH PERFORMANCE DESIGN, 3 YEARS, (70-90 STUDENTS)
MA COSTUME,1 YEAR, (2-6 STUDENTS)
DEADLINE: 15TH JANUARY (BA COURSES)
The Arts University College at Bournemouth, established in 1885 as a specialist institution, is now a leading University College offering high quality specialist education in art, design, media and performance across the creative industries. We remain passionate about our subjects and continue to encourage curiosity, risk-taking and adventure in exploring and pushing subject knowledge and its boundaries. The Arts University College provides staff and students with a well resourced environment in which to practise to the highest professional standards. AUCB is one of only fifteen higher education institutions in the UK devoted solely to the study of art, design and media. The University College has been providing specialist education for over a century and enjoys a strong reputation, both nationally and internationally.

BATH SPA UNIVERSITY
NEWTON PARK
NEWTON ST LOE
BATH BA2 9BN
TEL: 01225 875 875
ENQUIRIES@BATHSPA.AC.UK
WWW.BATHSPA.AC.UK
SJP MEMBERS: **164**
COURSES: BA (HONS) THEATRE PRODUCTION, 3 YEARS, (15-30 STUDENTS)
DEADLINE: 15TH JANUARY
Bath Spa University offers pre-degree study, undergraduate degrees and post-graduate degrees in a wide range of programmes. We are a teaching-led university with an emphasis on teaching of the highest quality. In each of our

Testimonial about Bath Spa University by John Celea:
"The course was a very comprehensive and intensive three year commitment. It is the most worthwhile thing I have done so far in my life."

Training

Schools of study there are programmes with outstanding results in sector-wide quality assurance processes. The University has achieved exceptionally high rankings in national newspaper league tables. Its popularity is growing each year, and in the past five years it has achieved a 40% increase in under-graduate applications. With around 7,000 students the University is small enough for students to benefit from a supportive and friendly study environment, but large enough to provide excellent facilities and resources. Its campuses are superb.

BIRKBECK, UNIVERSITY OF LONDON
MALET STREET, BLOOMSBURY
LONDON WC1E 7HX
TEL: 020 7631 6000
ENGLISHANDHUMANITIES@BBK.AC.UK
WWW.BBK.AC.UK
SJP MEMBERS: **76**
COURSES: BA (HONS) THEATRE & DRAMA
STUDIES, 4 YEARS
BA (HONS) THEATRE STUDIES & ENGLISH, 4 YEARS
MA CREATIVE PRODUCING
MA CREATIVE WRITING
MA SHAKESPEARE AND CONTEMPORARY PERFORMANCE
MFA THEATRE DIRECTING, 2 YEARS
MA TEXT AND PERFORMANCE (WITH RADA), 1 YEAR FULL-TIME, 2 YEARS PART-TIME
DEADLINE: 15TH JANUARY (BA COURSES)

Birkbeck is a world-class research and teaching institution, a vibrant centre of academic excellence and London's only specialist provider of evening higher education. A global elite, top 150 institution, we encourage applications from students without traditional qualifi-cations. Nearly 18,000 students studied at Birkbeck in 2010-2011 (4,683 under-graduates, 5,075 postgraduates, and 8,064 certificate students).

Testimonial about Birkbeck College, University of London by Oliver Stephens-Ofner:

"I was very impressed by this course and received a great amount of encouragement from the academic staff. I learnt how to write scripts which I am now doing professionally and I am currently developing a feature film. I also found other aspects of the course interesting such as British cinema history and a study of the press in the media analysis module. My favourite part of the course was TV studio workshop in which we created our own TV shows. Overall the course taught me a lot and has boosted my confidence."

Bristol Old Vic Theatre School

1 – 2 DOWNSIDE ROAD
BRISTOL BS8 2XF
TEL: 0117 973 3535
ENQUIRIES@OLDVIC.AC.UK
WWW.OLDVIC.AC.UK
SJP MEMBERS: **372**
COURSES: FdA COSTUME FOR THEATRE,
TELEVISION AND FILM, 2 YEARS
* BA (HONS) PROFESSIONAL STAGE
MANAGEMENT, 3 YEARS; PG DIP THEATRE ARTS
MANAGEMENT, 1 YEAR; PG DIP THEATRE
PRODUCTION MANAGEMENT, 1 YEAR
PG DIP SCENIC ART, 1 YEAR
MA PROFESSIONAL THEATRE DESIGN, 1 YEAR

MA DRAMA DIRECTING, 1 YEAR
DEADLINE: 15TH JANUARY (BA COURSES)
Opened by Laurence Olivier in 1946, the school is an industry-led vocational training establishment preparing students for careers in acting, stage management, costume, design, scenic art, directing, theatre arts management, production management, lighting, electrics, sound, studio management, propmaking, VT editing and scenic construction. The School is unique in that it is staffed by working professionals and trains people for all disciplines, working together within one organisation.

Testimonial about Bristol Old Vic Theatre School by Lucy Wilkinson:

"An intense year that equipped me well for designing as a career. I learned, and learn, a lot on each job, but I haven't been out of work since I graduated thanks to that solid training and the nurture of an inbuilt faith which you definitely need to do this job."

You can check out the theatre company Lucy helped to found at **www.jerichohouse.org.uk**.

Testimonial about Bristol Old Vic Theatre School by Daphne Bates:

"This was a very good hands-on Stage Management course. We started putting on shows as soon as we started the course which was such good experience for us. I thoroughly enjoyed the course and learnt so much from it."

Testimonial about Bristol Old Vic Theatre School by Abi Kennedy:

"A hands on, vocational course involving pattern cutting, costume construction, millinery, tailoring, costume buying and hire, costume supervision and much more. A varied and exciting course which fully prepares you for the professional theatre world. Highly recommended."

BRIT School of Performing Arts
60 The Crescent
Croydon CR0 2HN
Tel: 020 8665 5242
admin@brit.croydon.sch.uk
www.brit.croydon.sch.uk
SJP members: **130**
Courses: BTEC Technical Theatre Arts, 2 years

The BRIT School is Britain's only FREE Performing Arts and Technology School. It is an independent, state funded City College for the Technology of the Arts, the only one of its kind dedicated to education and vocational training for the performing arts, media, art and design and the technologies that make performance possible. As a school for 14-19 year olds, we are unique and pioneering in our approach to education, but we are not a stage or fame school. We recognise that most of our students intend to make a career in the arts, entertainment and communications industries, but the school expects all to follow full time courses to completion. It is a vocational school; if an applicant is determined on a life devoted to art, dance, music, radio, television/film or theatre, then this could well be the right place.

Brunel University
Kingston Lane
Uxbridge
Middlesex UB8 3PH
Tel: 01895 274 000
admissions@brunel.ac.uk
www.brunel.ac.uk
SJP members: **98**
Courses: BA (Hons) Theatre, 3 years
BA (Hons) Theatre and Creative Writing, 3 years
BA (Hons) Theatre and English, 3 years full-time, 4 ½-6 years part-time
BA (Hons) Theatre and Film and Television Studies, 3 years full-time, 4 ½-6 years part-time
BA (Hons) Theatre and Games Design, 3 years full-time, 4 ½-6 years part-time
BA (Hons) Creative Writing, 3 years full-time, 4 ½-6 years part-time
MA Contemporary Performance Making, 1 year full-time, 2 years part-time
Deadline: January 15th (BA Courses)

Brunel is a world-class university based in Uxbridge, West London. Now over 40 years old, our mission has always been to combine academic rigour with the practical, entrepreneurial and imaginative approach pioneered by our namesake Isambard Kingdom Brunel.

Testimonial about BRIT School for Performing Arts by James Washer (Technical Theatre Arts):

"What a truly awesome two years it's been, I can't stress how good this course is at BRIT. What we were able to achieve and learn is incredible."

CENTRAL SCHOOL OF SPEECH & DRAMA
ETON AVENUE
LONDON NW3 3HY
TEL: 020 7722 8183
ENQUIRIES@CSSD.AC.UK
WWW.CSSD.AC.UK
SJP MEMBERS: **1,164**
COURSES: *BA (HONS) COSTUME CONSTRUCTION, 3 YEARS
BA (HONS) DESIGN FOR THE STAGE, 3 YEARS
BA (HONS) PERFORMANCE ARTS, 3 YEARS
*BA (HONS) PRODUCTION LIGHTING, 3 YEARS
*BA (HONS) PROP MAKING, 3 YEARS
BA (HONS) PUPPETRY, 3 YEARS
*BA (HONS) SCENIC ART, 3 YEARS
*BA (HONS) SCENIC CONSTRUCTION, 3 YEARS
*BA (HONS) STAGE MANAGEMENT, 3 YEARS
*BA (HONS) TECHNICAL AND PRODUCTION MANAGEMENT, 3 YEARS
BA (HONS) THEATRE LIGHTING DESIGN, 3 YEARS

*BA (HONS) THEATRE SOUND, 3 YEARS
MA ADVANCED THEATRE PRACTICE, 1 YEAR
MA APPLIED THEATRE, 1 YEAR FULL-TIME, 2 YEARS PART-TIME
MA CREATIVE PRODUCING, 1 YEAR
MA MUSIC THEATRE, 1 YEAR
MA SCENOGRAPHY, 1 YEAR FULL-TIME, 2 YEARS PART-TIME
MA/MFA WRITING FOR STAGE AND BROADCAST MEDIA, 1 YEAR FULL-TIME, 2 YEARS PART-TIME
DEADLINE: 15TH JANUARY (BA COURSES)

With over 55 academic staff, together with visiting artists and lecturers, Central contains the largest grouping of drama/theatre/performance specialists in the UK, who make a major contribution to research in their various disciplines. Its special strength, unique in the sector, lies in a combination of first-rate practical training and production, with a highly

Testimonial posted by Steven Woolmer, 2006, BA (Hons) Technical and Production Manager:

"CSSD is a superb place to gain valuable knowledge of your chosen discipline, supervised by Professional lecturers, with real industry experience. An excellent place to get a good foundation for the rest of your career."

Steve's website is **www.sw-productions.co.uk**.

Testimonial about Central School of Speech and Drama by Alexandra Isaacs:

"Central has been a springboard for my career providing me with the essential skills, as well as varied opportunities and contacts for career longevity."

Testimonial about Central School of Speech and Drama by Daniel Harries:

"Brilliant opportunities and fantastic experience."

ranked programme of research – research aimed at the cutting edge of new performance practice. Central undoubtedly has the largest and most diverse faculty of specialist, expert staff and the broadest portfolio of drama, theatre and performance-related programmes in Europe. As well as meeting high academic standards, Central's courses work to professional theatre standards. Where theatre production work forms part of a course, the School employs a company ethos that respects all collaborators in a production alike, whether actor, designer, technician or outreach worker organising an educational workshop for a special needs school. Professional directors and designers will often work alongside students, or as mentors on projects. Where appropriate, programmes meet rigorous vocational criteria set by professional accrediting bodies.

CITY LIT

KEELEY STREET
COVENT GARDEN
LONDON
WC2B 4BA
TEL: 020 7831 7831
INFOLINE@CITYLIT.AC.UK
WWW.CITYLIT.AC.UK
SJP MEMBERS: **139**

COURSES: FOUNDATION DEGREE TECHNICAL THEATRE SKILLS, 34 WEEKS
DIRECTORS' WORKSHOP, 2 WEEKS
FIGHTING FOR FILM, 17 WEEKS
City Lit is London's ultimate destination for inspiring evening, daytime and weekend courses for adults. Each year we offer thousands of part-time courses, always trying to follow new trends and the passions and interests of our learners. Most of our classes take place in our bright, modern flagship building in Covent Garden and are taught by inspiring teachers, many of whom are leading experts and practitioners in their field.

COVENTRY UNIVERSITY

PRIORY STREET
COVENTRY CV1 5FB
TEL: 024 7688 7688
STUDENTENQUIRIES@COVENTRY.AC.UK
WWW.COVENTRY.AC.UK
SJP MEMBERS: **112**
COURSES: BA (HONS) DANCE MAKING AND PERFORMANCE, 3 YEARS FULL-TIME, 4 YEARS SANDWICH COURSE OR STUDY ABROAD
BA (HONS) THEATRE AND PROFESSIONAL PRACTICE, 3 YEARS
BA (HONS) MUSIC COMPOSITION, 3 YEARS FULL-TIME, 4 YEARS SANDWICH COURSE OR STUDY ABROAD
MA/PG DIP/PG CERTS CONTEMPORARY ARTS

Testimonial about City Lit by Anna Cordell:
"Great course, well organised, constructive and fun. Interesting anecdotes and actual radio experience from the tutor."

PRACTICE, 1 YEAR FULL-TIME, 2 YEARS PART-TIME
DEADLINE: 15TH JANUARY (BA COURSES)
We are proud to offer a range of courses
that approach the performing arts from a
variety of perspectives and that provide
valuable professional experience,
enabling graduates to thrive in a
demanding and competitive field. We
encourage experimentation, curiosity and
investigation and are distinguished by
our strong practical focus and complementary emphasis on the study and
analysis of the professional context for
performing arts activity. Our Performing
Arts facilities are among the best in the
country. With dedicated performance
spaces for dance, music and theatre, as
well as a number of rehearsal rooms,
dance studios, music practise and
seminar rooms, students get a taste of
what it's like to be a professional.
Our highly qualified staff of
dancers/choreographers, composers,
performers, actors, arts administrators
and researchers enjoy local, national and,
in some cases, international reputations
for innovative practice and leadership in
their fields. The supportive and friendly
atmosphere we foster encourages and
provides considerable possibilities for col-
laborative work across all the arts.

DE MONTFORT UNIVERSITY, LEICESTER
THE GATEWAY
LEICESTER LE1 9BH
TEL: 0116 255 1551
ENQUIRY@DMU.AC.UK
WWW.DMU.AC.UK
SJP MEMBERS: **268**
COURSES: FDSC CREATIVE SOUND TECHNOLOGY,
2 YEARS
BA (HONS) MUSIC, TECHNOLOGY AND
PERFORMANCE, 3 YEARS FULL-TIME, 6 YEARS
PART-TIME
DEADLINE: 15TH JANUARY (BA COURSE)
Thousands of lives are changed for the
better every year through the inspira-
tional teaching and vital research taking
place at De Montfort University (DMU).
The School of Arts at De Montfort
University encompasses performance
arts, visual arts and arts management
courses, offering undergraduate and
postgraduate study that encourages a
cutting-edge approach to contemporary
practice together with strong academic

Testimonial about De Montfort University, Leicester by Peter Wellington:
"I enjoyed this course a lot, it stretched my imagination. During the course I learnt a lot about the science of sound; how sound works in particular spaces etc. I also learnt a lot about the intricacies of working in a studio environment, using the software/hardware etc."
Peter's website is **www.myspace.com/mwpulse**.

critical enquiry and analysis. Study within the School is underpinned by our academic staff many of whom are active practitioners and leading researchers. Our high-grade teaching provides an innovative and creative learning environment.

EAST 15 ACTING SCHOOL

HATFIELDS
RECTORY LANE
LOUGHTON IG10 3RY
TEL: 020 8508 5983
EAST15@ESSEX.AC.UK
WWW.EAST15.AC.UK
SJP MEMBERS: **217**
COURSES: FDA/BA STAGE MANAGEMENT AND TECHNICAL THEATRE, 3 YEARS
MA IN THEATRE DIRECTING, 1 YEAR
MFA IN THEATRE DIRECTING, 2 YEARS
DEADLINE: 15TH JANUARY (BA COURSE)

For 50 years, East 15 Acting School has produced actors, directors, producers and theatre technicians for stage, TV, film and radio including Oscar nominee Stephen Daldry, award winning director of Billy Elliot, The Hours and The Reader. In September 2000, East 15 merged with the University of Essex, opening an exciting new chapter in the history of both institutions and offering new opportunities to students. Several million pounds have been spent on new buildings and facilities at East 15 on both campuses since then, including the purchase of a Victorian gothic church in Southend which has now been converted into a state-of-the-art theatre and performance space, and re-named The Clifftown Theatre and Studios. East 15 continues to move from strength to strength, with the two exciting campuses in Loughton and Southend, plus a range of innovative and unique undergraduate and postgraduate schemes, many of which are NCDT accredited. This has been reflected in recent and successful surveys, with undergraduate students at East 15 responding positively about their experiences as part of the National Student Satisfaction Survey and Student Satisfaction Survey, while postgraduates responded positively as part of the Student Satisfaction Survey.

GOLDSMITHS, UNIVERSITY OF LONDON

NEW CROSS
LONDON SE14 6NW
TEL: 020 7919 7171
COURSE-INFO@GOLD.AC.UK
WWW.GOLD.AC.UK
SJP MEMBERS: **432**
COURSES: BA (HONS) DRAMA & THEATRE ARTS, 3 YEARS
DEADLINE: 15TH JANUARY

We educate tomorrow's Theatre and Performance professionals. TaP graduates are broad-minded, informed and

---

Testimonial about East 15 Acting School by Thomas Edward-Bennett:

"Fantastic foundation course. I learned so much."

articulate, possessed with a range of intellectual, creative and life skills. Many find jobs across the cultural industries whilst many also pursue successful freelance careers. Recent graduates have won prestigious awards as playwrights, directors, creators of new work and cultural leaders in the UK and internationally. Studying the discipline in a university such as Goldsmiths offers you all the advantages of a uniquely creative intellectual community in which to develop knowledge, experience and the ability to forge a professional future.
Testimonial about Goldsmiths, University of London by Rowena Wallace
The course is very well-rounded giving you a wide variety of skills not only as a performer, but also in production, direction and stage management.

GUILDFORD SCHOOL OF ACTING (GSA)
STAG HILL CAMPUS, GUILDFORD
SURREY GU2 7XH
TEL: 01483 684 040
GSAENQUIRIES@GSA.SURREY.AC.UK
WWW.CONSERVATOIRE.ORG
SJP MEMBERS: **345**
COURSES: * DIPLOMA IN PROFESSIONAL PRODUCTION SKILLS, 2 YEARS
BA (HONS) PROFESSIONAL PRODUCTION SKILLS, 3 YEARS
DEADLINE: 15TH JANUARY (BA COURSE)
GSA has built an international reputation for excellence in training for actors and technicians in all areas of theatre and the recorded media. GSA provides vocational training with nationally recognised qualifications. All two and three years courses are validated by either Trinity College, London or the University of Surrey. GSA offers the very best vocational training in Acting, Musical Theatre and Stage Management with courses ranging from National Diplomas and Foundation Degrees through to Post Graduate quali-

---

Testimonial about Goldsmiths, University of London by Poppy Woods:
"Excellent course teaching me all the skills relevant for pursuing a career within the performing arts industries."

Testimonial about Goldsmiths, University of London by Cristina Sartorio:
"I would recommend Goldsmiths University to anyone. I thoroughly enjoyed my studying experience there and, above all they provided me with all the skills and confidence I needed to work in any creative environment."

fications. New state of the art facilities for Stage Management, film making, a number of theatres and a very special creative community make GSA a top choice amongst candidates wishing to train for the performing arts industry.

GUILDHALL SCHOOL OF MUSIC AND DRAMA
SILK STREET
BARBICAN
LONDON EC2Y 8DT
TEL: 020 7628 2571
DRAMA@GSMD.AC.UK
WWW.GSMD.AC.UK
SJP MEMBERS: **358**
COURSES: * BA (HONS) TECHNICAL THEATRE – STAGE MANAGEMENT, 3 YEARS
BA (HONS) TECHNICAL THEATRE – THEATRE TECHNOLOGY, 3 YEARS
BA (HONS) TECHNICAL THEATRE – DESIGN REALISATION, 3 YEARS
DEADLINE: 15TH JANUARY

The Guildhall School of Music & Drama is one of Europe's leading conservatoires, offering musicians, actors, stage managers and theatre technicians an inspiring environment in which to develop as artists and professionals. The School first opened its doors on 27 September 1880 to 62 part-time students in a disused warehouse in the City of London. Today it is situated in the heart of one of Britain's most important arts venues at the Barbican and has over 800 full-time music and drama students, with a growing international reputation for its teaching and research.

HULL COLLEGE
QUEEN'S GARDENS
HULL HU1 3DG
TEL: 01482 598 744
INFO@HULL-COLLEGE.AC.UK
WWW.HULL-COLLEGE.AC.UK
SJP MEMBERS: **83**
COURSES: FDA STAGE MANAGEMENT AND TECHNICAL THEATRE, 2 YEARS
FDA COSTUME DESIGN AND INTERPRETATION, 2 YEARS FULL-TIME, 3 YEARS PART-TIME
BTEC LEVEL 3 EXTENDED DIPLOMA IN PRODUCTION ARTS (STAGE MANAGEMENT), 2 YEARS
BA (HONS) STAGE MANAGEMENT AND TECHNICAL THEATRE (TOP-UP), 1 YEAR
DEADLINE: 15TH JANUARY

Whatever your age, your lifestyle, commitments or ambition Hull College can help you gain the skills and qualifications you need to set you on the pathway to career success. Students at the College study on a wide variety of further and higher education courses, from A Levels to NVQs, Foundation Degrees and Degrees, full-time or part-time, in subjects ranging from Business, Engineering, and Performing Arts to Health and Social Care. You can be sure that from the time you arrive you will find experienced tutors providing the highest standards for learning and excellent opportunities to progress your dream job or place at University.

LANCASTER UNIVERSITY

BAILRIGG
LANCASTER LA1 4YW
TEL: 01524 65201
LICA-ENQUIRIES@LANCASTER.AC.UK
WWW.LANCS.AC.UK
SJP MEMBERS: **128**
COURSES: BA (HONS) THEATRE STUDIES, 3 YEARS
BA (HONS) THEATRE STUDIES AND ENGLISH
LITERATURE, 3 YEARS, (35 STUDENTS OVER BOTH
COURSES)
DEADLINE: 15TH JANUARY

Theatre Studies at Lancaster is acknowledged as a UK leader in the study of innovative contemporary performance and its role in culture. As a constituent part of Lancaster Institute for the Contemporary Arts (LICA), Theatre Studies ensures the practice of theatre and performance is central to what we do. Our approach is characterised by both the interrogation of the relationship between theory and practice, and the investigation of drama, theatre and performance of the twentieth and twenty-first centuries.

LEWISHAM COLLEGE

LEWISHAM WAY
LONDON SE4 1UT
TEL: 0800 834 545
ENQUIRIES@LEWISHAM.AC.UK
WWW.LEWISHAM.AC.UK
SJP MEMBERS: **78**
COURSES: BTEC DRAMA LEVEL 2, 1 YEAR
BTEC DRAMA LEVEL 3, 1 YEAR
EXTENDED DIPLOMA PERFORMING ARTS LEVEL 3, 1 YEAR
SUBSIDIARY DIPLOMA PERFORMING ARTS LEVEL 3, 1 YEAR
SUBSIDIARY AWARD TECHNICAL THEATRE, 1 YEAR
DEADLINE: 15TH JANUARY (BA COURSES)

Lewisham College is a large and very successful further education college in South East London. Our mission is creating successful futures. We are a large vocational college. From our two sites, we work with many diverse partners, including: schools, universities, trade unions, businesses and a range of public sector organisations. Our reputation for innovation and excellence was formally recognised when we were first awarded Beacon Status in 1999. We now have four Beacon awards. We've recently been awarded the Artsmark by Arts Council England. The Artsmark is a national award that accredits quality arts education. It is Arts Council England's flagship programme to enable educational establishments to celebrate and develop high quality arts education. We're also a Founder College of the National Skills Academy Creative & Cultural giving our drama, technical theatre and music students access to the the best opportunities the UK creative industries can offer.

LIVERPOOL HOPE UNIVERSITY

HOPE PARK
LIVERPOOL L16 9JD
TEL: 0151 291 3000
ENQUIRY@HOPE.AC.UK
WWW.HOPE.AC.UK
SJP MEMBERS: **71**
COURSES: BA (HONS) CREATIVE AND
PERFORMING ARTS, 3 YEARS
BA (HONS) DRAMA AND THEATRE STUDIES, 3
YEARS
MA CONTEMPORARY POPULAR THEATRE, 2-2 ½
YEARS
DEADLINE: 15TH JANUARY (BA COURSES)
With a history extending 168 years,
Liverpool Hope has developed a strong
tradition of scholarship and research in
key disciplines. As the only ecumenical
university foundation in Europe the
University's work has been shaped by
Christian principles but embraces those of
all faiths and none. The excellent academic
record of our students and supportive
pastoral care and, as one of Britain's
smaller universities, Liverpool Hope values
the individual. Care, concern and support
for students are always a priority. The
University places great emphasis on the
bringing together of research excellence
and top-quality teaching. This is facilitated
by a community of academics and
scholars who are of the highest calibre.
This research-informed teaching enables
our students to develop into rounded and
employable graduates who can take their
place confidently as global citizens in the
21st century.

LIVERPOOL INSTITUTE OF PERFORMING ARTS

MOUNT STREET
LIVERPOOL L1 9HF
TEL: 0151 330 3000
RECEPTION@LIPA.AC.UK
WWW.LIPA.AC.UK
SJP MEMBERS: **362**
COURSES: BA (HONS) MUSIC, THEATRE AND
ENTERTAINMENT MANAGEMENT, 3 YEARS, (30
STUDENTS)
BA (HONS) THEATRE AND PERFORMANCE
TECHNOLOGY, 3 YEARS, (30 STUDENTS)
BA (HONS) THEATRE AND PERFORMANCE DESIGN
BA (HONS) SOUND TECHNOLOGY
DEADLINE: 15TH JANUARY
The Liverpool Institute for Performing
Arts opened in 1996 to forge a new
approach to performing arts training. It
was co-founded by our Lead Patron Sir
Paul McCartney and Mark Featherstone-
Witty (LIPA's Principal), and is housed in
his old school, which underwent a multi-
million pound renovation to transform it
into a state-of-the-art performing arts

**Testimonial about Liverpool Institute of Performing Arts posted by
James Bentley, 2010, Sound Technology:**
*"Amazing place, amazing staff and amazing students! Great
place to learn your trade!"*

higher education institution. Today LIPA is an acknowledged part of the UK's higher education provision for the performing arts, recognised and ranked alongside institutions a lot older. LIPA provides education and training for the main skills needed for putting on a show (performers and those who makes performance possible), uniquely blending specialist and generic skills. We train students for a future of sustained employment. Most recent figures have shown that over the most recent four year period, 96% of LIPA's graduates are in work three years after leaving, while 87% work in the performing arts. To achieve this, our curriculum is constantly being revised.

LIVERPOOL JOHN MOORES UNIVERSITY
KINGSWAY HOUSE
2ND FLOOR, HATTON GARDEN
LIVERPOOL L3 2AJ
TEL: 0151 231 2121
COURSES@LJMU.AC.UK
WWW.LJMU.AC.UK
SJP MEMBERS: **128**
COURSES: BA (HONS) DRAMA, 3 YEARS, (50 STUDENTS)
BA (HONS) DRAMA AND CREATIVE WRITING, 3 YEARS, (10 STUDENTS)
DEADLINE: 15TH JANUARY
The Liverpool Screen School offers undergraduate courses in Creative Writing, Drama, Film Studies, Journalism and Media Professional Studies and postgraduate courses in International Journalism, Screen and Interactive Media, Writing and Screenwriting. We also pride ourselves in developing a warm and friendly environment with a strong commitment to nurturing and supporting creativity whilst offering excellent learning resources and first-class student support. You will be taught by professional, experienced and enthusiastic academic staff with extensive and current practical industry experience. As well as being a thriving academic community the School has strong links with local, national and international media companies and institutions including the BBC, Trinity Mirror, and Lime Pictures. These productive working relationships include providing students with opportunities for work placements and research projects. This network of partners will allow you to establish links within the professional field in which your future career will develop. Liverpool is a city that has something for everyone and is very supportive of the 50,000 students who live, work and study in its universities.

London Academy of Music and Dramatic Art (LAMDA)

155 Talgarth Road
London W14 9DA
Tel: 020 8834 0500
enquiries@lamda.org.uk
www.lamda.org.uk
SJP members: **366**
Courses: * Foundation Degree Stage Management & Technical Theatre, 2 years
Diploma Directors, 1 year, (4 students)
Diploma Designers, 1 year, (1 student)
Deadline: 1st March

LAMDA is an independent drama school, dedicated to the vocational training of actors, stage managers and technicians, directors and designers in the skills and levels of creativity necessary to meet the highest demands and best opportunities in theatre, film, radio and TV. The group work ethic is central to LAMDA's teaching. The training does not deconstruct the student in order to rebuild a LAMDA product but encourages and develops innate skills. The courses are practical not academic. LAMDA welcomes applications from all sections of the community regardless of ethnicity, religion, gender or disability.
Testimonial about London Academy of Music and Dramatic Art by Sam Shuck
A great course. A thorough grounding of all aspects of technical theatre. Full support from tutors/able to specialise in more than one theatrical role in the second year; purely practical.

London College of Fashion

20 John Prince's Street
London W1G 0BJ
Tel: 020 7514 7400
enquiries@fashion.arts.ac.uk
www.fashion.arts.ac.uk
SJP members: **719**
Courses: BA (Hons) Costume for Performance, 3 years, (17 Students)
BA (Hons) Make Up and Prosthetics for Performance, 3 years, (21 Students)
BA (Hons) Technical Effects for Performance, 3 years, (17 Students)
MA Costume Design for performance, 15 months full-time, 27 months part-time
Deadline: 15th January (BA Courses)
London College of Fashion's rich heritage and responsiveness to changes in design practice have positioned it as a leading global provider of fashion education, research and consultancy. The College's work is centred on the development of ideas: its staff and students use fashion alongside historical and cultural practice to challenge social, political and ethical agendas. This, combined with its forward-thinking business and management portfolio and its relationship with the global fashion and lifestyle industries, is the underpinning of its mission to "Fashion the Future".

152

LOUGHBOROUGH UNIVERSITY

LOUGHBOROUGH UNIVERSITY
LEICESTERSHIRE LE11 3TU
TEL: 01509 263 171
EANDDUNDERGRADUATE@LBORO.AC.UK
WWW.LBORO.AC.UK
SJP MEMBERS: **106**
COURSES: BA (HONS) DRAMA, 3 YEARS
BA (HONS) DRAMA WITH ENGLISH, 3 YEARS
BA (HONS) DRAMA WITH BUSINESS STUDIES, 3
YEARS
MA DRAMA, 1 YEAR
MA CREATIVE WRITING, 1 YEAR FULL-TIME, 2
YEARS PART-TIME
DEADLINE: 15TH JANUARY (BA COURSES)
Loughborough is a fantastic place to
study and work, boasting unrivalled
sporting achievement, internationally
acclaimed research and outstanding
teaching quality – attributes that helped
us to secure the prestigious Sunday Times
'2008/2009 University of the Year' award.
Our attractive single-site campus
provides an environment that is
stimulating and supportive, offering first-
rate facilities for both students and staff.
There is a real pride in the University that
touches everyone associated with it.

MIDDLESEX UNIVERSITY

THE BURROUGHS
LONDON
NW4 4BT
TEL: 020 8411 5555
ENQUIRIES@MDX.AC.UK
WWW.MDX.AC.UK
SJP MEMBERS: **481**
COURSES: BA (HONS) THEATRE ARTS (DESIGN
AND TECHNICAL THEATRE), 3 YEARS
BA (HONS) THEATRE ARTS (THEATRE DIRECTING),
3 YEARS
DEADLINE: 15TH JANUARY
We are dedicated to unlocking potential
– in our students, through our research
and within businesses. We teach more
than 40,000 students on Middlesex
courses in London, Dubai, Mauritius and
with partners across the world. We have
a reputation for the highest quality
teaching, research that makes a real
difference to people's lives and a
practical, innovative approach to working
with businesses to develop staff potential
and provide solutions to business issues.
Our expertise is wide ranging, from
engineering, information, health and
social sciences, to business, arts and
education – and we're national leaders
in work based learning solutions.

MOUNTVIEW ACADEMY OF THEATRE ARTS

RALPH RICHARDSON MEMORIAL STUDIOS
CLARENDON ROAD, WOOD GREEN
LONDON N22 6XF
TEL: 020 8881 2201
ENQUIRIES@MOUNTVIEW.ORG.UK
WWW.MOUNTVIEW.ORG.UK
SJP MEMBERS: **526**
COURSES: BA (HONS) THEATRE PRODUCTION
ARTS, 2 YEARS
NATIONAL DIPLOMA PROFESSIONAL PRODUCTION
SKILLS, 2 YEARS
PG DIP TECHNICAL THEATRE, 1 YEAR
MA/PG DIP THEATRE DIRECTING, 1 YEAR
DEADLINE: 15TH JANUARY (BA COURSES)
Mountview Academy of Theatre Arts is
one of the UK's leading drama schools
with a worldwide reputation for
excellence in education and training.
Founded in 1945, Mountview offers
extensive and stimulating training for
those interested in pursuing a
Performance, Directing or Technical
Theatre career. The courses are
structured to give students a thorough
grounding in all aspects of their chosen
field. Students are trained to a high level
to develop a range of skills which will
enable them to bring thought, energy
and commitment to their professional
work, giving them the tools to succeed in
a competitive industry.

NEWCASTLE COLLEGE

RYE HILL CAMPUS
SCOTSWOOD ROAD
NEWCASTLE UPON TYNE NE4 7SA
TEL: 0191 200 4000
ENQUIRIES@NCL-COLL.AC.UK
WWW.NCL-COLL.AC.UK
SJP MEMBERS: **203**
COURSES: FDA LIVE MUSIC AND THEATRE
PRODUCTION, 2 YEARS
At Newcastle College teaching and
student support are second to none and
we have amazing campuses with a
fantastic variety of state-of-the-art
facilities including: An all new Sixth Form
College – opening 2013; A world-class
Renewable Energies Academy – based at
Wallsend riverside; £21million
Performance Academy – for music, media
and performing arts; Mandela Building –
purpose built for art, design and the
creative industries. Choosing a course is
a huge decision – one that can ultimately
change your life... so, it's good to know
that you've chosen the right place to
study!

NORTHBROOK COLLEGE

LITTLEHAMPTON ROAD
WORTHING BN12 6NU
TEL: 0845 155 6060
ENQUIRIES@NBCOL.AC.UK
WWW.NORTHBROOK.AC.UK
SJP MEMBERS: **173**
COURSES: FOUNDATION DEGREE PRODUCTION DESIGN/PROP MAKING, 2 YEARS
FOUNDATION DEGREE MAKE-UP & HAIRSTYLING FOR THEATRE ARTS, 2 YEARS
FOUNDATION DEGREE THEATRE ARTS: PROP MAKING & SPECIAL EFFECTS, 2 YEARS
FOUNDATION DEGREE STAGE & PRODUCTION MANAGEMENT, 2 YEARS
FOUNDATION DEGREE LIGHTING & SOUND DESIGN, 2 YEARS
FOUNDATION DEGREE PRODUCTION DESIGN & REALISATION, 2 YEARS
FOUNDATION DEGREE COSTUME DESIGN AND REALISATION, 2 YEARS
FOUNDATION DEGREE VENUE AND EVENT MANAGEMENT, 2 YEARS
BA (HONS) THEATRE ARTS (THIRD YEAR TOP-UP FROM FOUNDATION DEGREE), 1 YEAR
DEADLINE: 15TH JANUARY

The Southern Theatre Arts Centre at Northbrook College is one of the leading centres for theatre education in southern England with over 350 full time students. Courses range across the spectrum of theatre disciplines and facilities are among the best in the country. Our partnership with the University of Brighton and great location ensure that students enjoy all the advantages of being at the heart of the UK's creative culture. The courses have been developed in close partnership with industry and the endorsement of professional bodies as well as those of alumni and government reviewers speak for the excellence of the provision.

NORTHUMBRIA UNIVERSITY

ELLISON PLACE
NEWCASTLE UPON TYNE NE1 8ST
TEL: 0191 232 6002
ER.ADMISSIONS@NORTHUMBRIA.AC.UK
WWW.NORTHUMBRIA.AC.UK
SJP MEMBERS: **129**
COURSES: BA (HONS) DRAMA, 3 YEARS
BA (HONS) DRAMA AND SCRIPTWRITING, 3 YEARS
DEADLINE: 15TH JANUARY

The School of Arts and Social Sciences offers an exciting range of courses covering the arts, humanities and social sciences at undergraduate and postgraduate level. Programmes are designed to offer a breadth of knowledge and thorough practical training where appropriate, providing students with a broad range of transferable skills. We are highly rated by our own students, having achieved high satisfaction levels across disciplines in the 2010 National Student Survey.

Testimonial about Northbrook College by Alec Jordan:

"Very helpful staff will go that extra mile to give you the support you need, even for activities outside of college."

NOTTINGHAM TRENT UNIVERSITY
BURTON STREET
NOTTINGHAM
NG1 4BU
TEL: 0115 941 8418
APPLICATIONS@NTU.AC.UK
WWW.NTU.AC.UK
SJP MEMBERS: **365**
COURSES: BA (HONS) THEATRE DESIGN, 3 YEARS
BA (HONS) COSTUME DESIGN AND MAKING, 3 YEARS
DEADLINE: 15TH JANUARY
Nottingham Trent University (NTU) is a public teaching and research university in Nottingham, United Kingdom. We have earned a reputation for outstanding graduate employability, excellent teaching standards, impressive Student Services, and a diverse but close-knit student community.

QUEEN MARGARET UNIVERSITY
QUEEN MARGARET UNIVERSITY DRIVE
MUSSELBURGH, EH21 6UU
TEL: 0131 474 0000
ADMISSIONS@QMU.AC.UK
WWW.QMU.AC.UK
SJP MEMBERS: **231**
COURSES: BA (HONS) COSTUME DESIGN AND CONSTRUCTION, 4 YEARS
BA (HONS) THEATRE AND FILM STUDIES, 4 YEARS
DEADLINE: 15TH JANUARY
QMU offers students a small and friendly community environment. We provide thoroughly relevant teaching and research which is designed to meet the changing needs of students, employers and society. Our new campus is the most sustainable in the UK. We have widely recognised expertise in the areas of health and rehabilitation; sustainable business and creativity and culture.

RAVENSBOURNE
6 PENROSE WAY
GREENWICH PENINSULA
LONDON SE10 0EW
TEL: 020 3040 3500
INFO@RAVE.AC.UK
WWW.RAVE.AC.UK
SJP MEMBERS: **75**
COURSES: BA (HONS) SOUND DESIGN, 3 YEARS
DEADLINE: 15TH JANUARY
Ravensbourne is a world-class digital destination developing talented individuals and leading-edge businesses

---

Testimonial about Nottingham Trent University by Sayarun Nehar:

"This diverse course has given me the opportunity to cover subjects which differ from one another, yet relate in many ways. Instead of focusing primarily on one subject, I have been able to cover various subject areas which is important when entering a working environment where a variety of skills and knowledge is needed."

through learning, skills, applied research, enterprise and innovation. We are a university sector college innovating in digital media and design, with a vocationally focused portfolio of courses, spanning fashion, television and broadcasting, interactive product design, architecture and environment design, graphic design, animation, moving image, music production for media and sound design. We are a centre of excellence, industry accredited and a Skillset Media Academy.

ROEHAMPTON UNIVERSITY

ERASMUS HOUSE
ROEHAMPTON LANE
LONDON SW15 5PU
TEL: 020 8392 3232
ENQUIRIES@ROEHAMPTON.AC.UK
WWW.ROEHAMPTON.AC.UK
SJP MEMBERS: **94**
COURSES: BA DRAMA, THEATRE AND PERFORMANCE, 3 YEARS FULL-TIME, 5-7 YEARS FULL-TIME
MA/MRES PERFORMANCE & CREATIVE RESEARCH, 1 YEAR
MRES CHOREOGRAPHY AND PERFORMANCE, 1 YEAR FULL-TIME, 2 YEARS PART-TIME
MPHIL/PHD DRAMA, THEATRE AND PERFORMANCE
DEADLINE: 15TH JANUARY (BA COURSE)
At the University of Roehampton there is a strong emphasis on supporting our students to reach their full potential and helping them to launch themselves onto successful graduate careers. The emphasis is on contact with academics who are internationally known for their work. Our graduate employment rates are among the best in London. Roehampton is the only campus university in London, located in the south-west of the city, about 30 minutes from the West End. Our campus offers excellent facilities for learning and teaching, and a wide range of opportunities for students to get involved, through volunteering, playing sport, or joining one of our many student societies. The University has a strong research profile, with a third of our research rated internationally excellent, and ranked as the best in the UK for our research in Biological Anthropology and Dance. Some 9,000 students attend the University, 25% of whom are postgraduates. There is a cosmopolitan atmosphere, with more than 130 different nationalities on campus. We have a proud history stretching back 170 years through our four Colleges. At the same time, we have a very contemporary outlook, preparing our students for success in the modern world.

Training

ROSE BRUFORD COLLEGE

LAMORBEY PARK
BURNT OAK LANE, SIDCUP
KENT DA15 9DF
TEL: 020 8308 2600
ENQUIRIES@BRUFORD.AC.UK
WWW.BRUFORD.AC.UK
SJP MEMBERS: **964**
COURSES: *BA (HONS) COSTUME PRODUCTION, 3 YEARS
BA (HONS) CREATIVE LIGHTING CONTROL, 3 YEARS
*BA (HONS) LIGHTING DESIGN, 3 YEARS
BA (HONS) PERFORMANCE SOUND, 3 YEARS
*BA (HONS) SCENIC ARTS, 3 YEARS
*BA (HONS) STAGE MANAGEMENT, 3 YEARS
*BA (HONS) THEATRE DESIGN, 3 YEARS
DEADLINE: 15TH JANUARY

Set in beautiful, protected parkland, just 25 minutes by train from the heart of London's West End, the Rose Bruford College campus clusters around the Grade II listed Lamorbey House and grounds with modern, purpose-built facilities. Our teaching and administrative staff are of the highest quality, reflecting a balance of expertise in education and professional practice. Practitioners drawn from professional theatre, film and television, the music industry and other complementary professions teach and lead projects on all programmes and provide graduates with a direct link to the creative industries. Vocational preparation is a key element of all degree study.

ROYAL ACADEMY OF DRAMATIC ART (RADA)

GOWER STREET
LONDON WC1E 6ED
TEL: 020 7636 7076
ENQUIRIES@RADA.AC.UK
WWW.RADA.AC.UK
SJP MEMBERS: **495**
COURSES: FDA TECHNICAL THEATRE AND STAGE MANAGEMENT, 2 YEARS, (30 STUDENTS)
PROPERTY MAKING, 1 YEAR, (3 STUDENTS)
SCENIC ART, 1 YEAR, (3 STUDENTS)
SCENIC CONSTRUCTION, 1 YEAR, (3 STUDENTS)
SOUND DESIGN FOR THE THEATRE, 2 YEARS, (3 STUDENTS)
STAGE ELECTRICS AND LIGHTING DESIGN, 1 YEAR, (3 STUDENTS)
THEATRE COSTUME, 2 YEARS
THEATRE DESIGN (SET & COSTUME), 2 YEARS, (3 STUDENTS)
LIGHTING DESIGN FOR THE THEATRE, 1 WEEK
PROPERTY MAKING FOR THE STAGE, 1 WEEK
SCENIC ART FOR THE THEATRE, 2 YEARS
SET AND COSTUME DESIGN FOR THE THEATRE, 1 WEEK
SOUND DESIGN FOR THE THEATRE, 2 YEARS
SCENIC CONSTRUCTION FOR THE THEATRE, 1 WEEK
MA THEATRE DIRECTING, 1 YEAR, (3 STUDENTS)
DEADLINE: 31ST MARCH

Testimonial about Rose Bruford College by Sylvia Darkwa-Ohemeng:

"Learned a lot from the course in terms of experience, not only in Uni but also the experience in other theatres we did plays in, e.g. The Unicorn Theatre and I especially loved the uni grounds."

158

The Royal Academy of Dramatic Art (RADA) offers vocational training for actors, stage managers, directors, designers and technical stage craft specialists. RADA was established in 1904 and has built an outstanding reputation as a world-renowned centre of excellence, offering the best possible facilities, exceptional teaching and strong links with the industries that employ our graduates. RADA's student population is a diverse community, united by a shared passion for theatre-making. The Academy prides itself both on the professional standard of its student productions, which are attended by agents, casting directors and theatre practitioners, and on their track-record of employment in theatre, film and television.

ROYAL HOLLOWAY, UNIVERSITY OF LONDON
EGHAM HILL
EGHAM TW20 0EX
TEL: 01784 434 455
LIAISON-OFFICE@RHUL.AC.UK
WWW.RHUL.AC.UK
SJP MEMBERS: **249**
COURSES: BA (HONS) ENGLISH AND DRAMA, 3 YEARS
BA (HONS) DRAMA AND THEATRE STUDIES, 3 YEARS
MA THEATRE, 1 YEAR
MA THEATRE (APPLIED DRAMA), 1 YEAR
MA THEATRE (DIRECTING), 1 YEAR
MA THEATRE (PHYSICAL THEATRE & PERFORMANCES), 1 YEAR
MA PLAYWRITING, 1 YEAR

DEADLINE: 15TH JANUARY (BA COURSES)
Drama at Royal Holloway is one of the most innovative, rigorous and lively academic departments in the world. Our sharp, innovative and creative students work with some of the country's leading scholars and theatremakers in first-class learning and performing spaces. A drama and theatre education at Royal Holloway is a full-time, immersive experience, and you'll be working with some of the leading experts in the field, both creatively and intellectually. Loads of our students have gone on to pursue successful careers in theatre – as makers, teachers, or both, but our students also go into arts admin, management and a host of other professional careers.

ROYAL CONSERVATOIRE OF SCOTLAND
100 RENFREW STREET
GLASGOW G2 3DB
TEL: 0141 332 8901
DRAMAADMISSIONS@RCS.AC.UK
WWW.RCS.AC.UK
SJP MEMBERS: **362**
COURSES: * BA TECHNICAL AND PRODUCTION ARTS, 3 YEARS
BA CONTEMPORARY PERFORMANCE PRACTICE, 4 YEARS
MA CLASSICAL AND CONTEMPORARY TEXT (DIRECTING), 1 YEAR, (4 STUDENTS)
DEADLINE: 15TH JANUARY (BA COURSES)
The Royal Conservatoire is Scotland's national centre of professional vocational training in performance arts. Our location is the heart of Glasgow; our orientation

is the contemporary international scene. We are leading the way as one of Europe's top conservatoires, offering a rare breadth of artistic disciplines. Everything we do is driven by our desire for excellence. Students flourish thanks to the extraordinary blend of intensive tuition, a rigorous performance schedule, working with professional counterparts in industry, and the space to create with others across the disciplines if they wish. Both students and staff are prolific in creating truly innovative new work.

globally, enabling students to enter and influence the world of music, theatre and related professions. The College is constantly pushing boundaries with innovative and exciting programmes of study tailored to the demands of contemporary arts and creative industries. In 2009, its 60th anniversary year, the College became the UK's first All-Steinway Conservatoire. The focus is always on the future and we take immense pride in the world-class talent of our students.

THE ROYAL WELSH COLLEGE OF MUSIC AND DRAMA
CASTLE GROUNDS
CATHAYS PARK
CARDIFF CF10 3ER
TEL: 029 2034 2854
ADMISSIONS@RWCMD.AC.UK
WWW.RWCMD.AC.UK
SJP MEMBERS: **490**
COURSES: * BA (HONS) STAGE MANAGEMENT, 3 YEARS, (20 STUDENTS)
BA (HONS) THEATRE DESIGN, 3 YEARS, (18 STUDENTS)
MA STAGE AND EVENT MANAGEMENT, 1 YEAR
MA THEATRE DESIGN, 1 YEAR, (7 STUDENTS)
MA ARTS MANAGEMENT, 1 YEAR
DEADLINE: 15TH JANUARY (BA COURSES)
The Royal Welsh College of Music & Drama, the National Conservatoire of Wales, and part of the Glamorgan Group, competes alongside an international peer group of conservatoires and specialist arts colleges for the best students

SOUTHAMPTON SOLENT UNIVERSITY
EAST PARK TERRACE
SOUTHAMPTON
HAMPSHIRE SO14 0YN
TEL: 023 8031 9000
ASK@SOLENT.AC.UK
WWW.SOLENT.AC.UK
SJP MEMBERS: **95**
COURSES: BA (HONS) PERFORMANCE, 3 YEARS
BA (HONS) EVENT MANAGEMENT, 3 YEARS
BA (HONS) SCREENWRITING, 3 YEARS
BA (HONS) ENGLISH AND SCREENWRITING, 3 YEARS
BA (HONS) SPECIAL EFFECTS, 3 YEARS
MA CREATIVE WRITING, 1 YEAR
DEADLINE: 15TH JANUARY (BA COURSES)
Southampton Solent University (SSU) is a dynamic and distinctive new university dedicated to academic excellence, social justice and the integration of theory and practice. 'Real world' experience is built into an exciting range of innovative courses, whether in business, technology,

art and design, media production, maritime, the creative industries, or sport. We have strong local roots within Southampton and its region, working closely with the city, the community, employers and voluntary organisations. The University is open, friendly and inclusive, with not surprisingly, given its great location and growing reputation, a strong international dimension. Overall, about one in five of our students come from Europe or overseas and seventy percent of the total student population comes from outside the Hampshire area. This makes for a lively, welcoming and stimulating place for work, study and relaxation.

STAFFORDSHIRE UNIVERSITY

COLLEGE ROAD, STOKE-ON-TRENT
STAFFORDSHIRE ST4 2DE
TEL: 01782 294 000
ENQUIRIES@STAFFS.AC.UK
WWW.STAFFS.AC.UK
SJP MEMBERS: **182**
COURSES: BA (HONS) THEATRE STUDIES AND TECHNICAL STAGE PRODUCTION, 3 YEARS
DEADLINE: 15TH JANUARY

Staffordshire University has a long and proud history of providing high quality, progressive and inclusive higher education for people from across Staffordshire, the region, the UK and the rest of the world. Studying in the Faculty of Arts, Media and Design provides students with an up-to-date, relevant and dynamic learning experience. We offer a broad portfolio of courses including "return to learn" pre-entry awards; full-time and part-time undergraduate degree programmes; postgraduate taught Masters and research MPhils and PhDs; and also Continuing Professional Development short courses.

UNIVERSITY COLLEGE FALMOUTH

WOODLANE, FALMOUTH
CORNWALL TR11 4RH
TEL: 01362 211 077
ADMISSIONS@FALMOUTH.AC.UK
WWW.FALMOUTH.AC.UK
SJP MEMBERS: **43**
COURSES: BA (HONS) THEATRE, 3 YEARS, (40 STUDENTS)
BA (HONS) CREATIVE EVENTS MANAGEMENT, 3 YEARS, (22 STUDENTS)
BA (HONS) CREATIVE WRITING, 3 YEARS, (30 STUDENTS)
BA (HONS) ENGLISH WITH CREATIVE WRITING, 3 YEARS, (35 STUDENTS)
MA PROFESSIONAL WRITING, 1 YEAR FULL-TIME, 2 YEARS PART-TIME, (30 STUDENTS)
DEADLINE: 15TH JANUARY (BA COURSES)

At University College Falmouth we

Testimonial about Staffordshire University by Matt Amison:

"The course is highly practical and so has offered me an intense insight into the production process."

Training

specialise in award winning Art, Design, Media, Performance and Writing courses at foundation, undergraduate and post-graduate level.

UNIVERSITY OF BIRMINGHAM
EDGBASTON
BIRMINGHAM B15 2TT
TEL: 0121 414 3344
ADMISSIONS@BHAM.AC.UK
WWW.BIRMINGHAM.AC.UK
SJP MEMBERS: **194**
COURSES: BA (HONS) DRAMA AND THEATRE ARTS, 3 YEARS
PHD DRAMA AND THEATRE STUDIES, 3 YEARS FULL-TIME, 6 YEARS PART-TIME
MA DRAMA AND THEATRE STUDIES, 1 YEAR FULL-TIME, 2 YEARS PART-TIME
MRES DRAMA AND THEATRE STUDIES, 1 YEAR FULL-TIME, 2 YEARS PART-TIME
MRES PLAYWRITING STUDIES, 1 YEAR, (15 STUDENTS)
DEADLINE: 15TH JANUARY (BA COURSE)
One of the best of the established British university drama departments, the Department of Drama and Theatre Arts at Birmingham enjoys a highly respected national and international reputation for excellence in teaching and research in the study of Drama. We were ranked 7th in the Guardian League Tables for 2011. The Department is a leader in practical theatre making, and places the role of the performer at the centre of the theatrical event. Students also acquire an all around theoretical knowledge of theatre, as well as direct experience of performance.

UNIVERSITY OF EAST ANGLIA
NORWICH RESEARCH PARK
NORWICH NR4 7TJ
TEL: 01603 456 161
ADMISSIONS@UEA.AC.UK
WWW.UEA.AC.UK
SJP MEMBERS: **116**
COURSES: BA (HONS) DRAMA, 3 YEARS
BA (HONS) ENGLISH LITERATURE AND DRAMA, 3 YEARS
BA (HONS) ENGLISH LITERATURE WITH CREATIVE WRITING, 3 YEARS
BA (HONS) SCRIPTWRITING AND PERFORMANCE, 3 YEARS
MA CREATIVE WRITING SCRIPTWRITING, 1 YEAR FULL-TIME, 2 YEARS PART-TIME
MA THEATRE DIRECTING: TEXT AND PRODUCTION, 1 YEAR FULL-TIME, 2 YEARS PART-TIME
DEADLINE: 15TH JANUARY (BA COURSES)

Testimonial about University College Falmouth by James Horrell
"I was impressed by both the college and the course. I now have a good understanding of various different roles within the media sector from editing and post production to online writing and scripting."

The School of Literature, Drama and Creative Writing at the University of East Anglia has a long-established international reputation in literary studies. World famous for its pioneering courses in creative writing, it is also home to prize-winning scholars and translators of literature and drama from all periods. Our unique approach to the study of literature and writing is powered by our conviction that – to quote Ezra Pound – 'literature is news that stays news'. At all levels of study, and on all degree courses, the School of Literature, Drama and Creative Writing at the University of East Anglia is the place where criticism and creativity go hand in hand.

UNIVERSITY OF GLASGOW

GLASGOW G12 8QQ
TEL: 0141 330 2000
STUDENT.RECRUITMENT@GLASGOW.AC.UK
WWW.GLA.AC.UK
SJP MEMBERS: **119**
COURSES: BA (HONS) THEATRE STUDIES, 4 YEARS
MLITT PLAYWRITING AND DRAMATURGY, 1 YEAR
MLITT THEATRE PRACTICES, 1 YEAR FULL-TIME, 2 YEARS PART-TIME
MLITT THEATRE STUDIES, 1 YEAR FULL-TIME, 2 YEARS PART-TIME
DEADLINE: 15TH JANUARY (BA COURSE)
Theatre, film and television studies at Glasgow is renowned for the highest quality research and teaching. The 2008 Research Assessment Exercise classified 85% of our research as world-leading or internationally excellent. We make use of our city's fantastic cultural resources. Glasgow is famed for its theatres and touring companies, its film and theatre venues, and its creative organisations. On campus, our facilities include a theatre, cinema, video editing suite and a design room for students. Our teaching methods combine theoretical, historical and practical approaches with the benefits of these excellent facilities. If you study with us, you will be taught in small seminar groups and supported to develop critical and creative skills that prepare you for a wide variety of careers.

UNIVERSITY OF HUDDERSFIELD

QUEENSGATE
HUDDERSFIELD WEST YORKSHIRE HD1 3DH
TEL: 01484 422 288
ADMISSIONSANDRECORDS@HUD.AC.UK
WWW.HUD.AC.UK
SJP MEMBERS: **90**
COURSES: FDA TECHNICAL THEATRE, 2 YEARS, (15 STUDENTS)
BA (HONS) COSTUME WITH TEXTILES, 3 YEARS FULL-TIME, 4 YEARS SANDWICH, (40 STUDENTS)
BA (HONS) TECHNICAL THEATRE, 3 YEARS, (25 STUDENTS)
BA (HONS) MUSIC WITH DRAMA, (10 STUDENTS)
BA (HONS) DRAMA, 3 YEARS FULL-TIME, 4 ½ YEARS PART-TIME, (50 STUDENTS)
MA COSTUME, 1 YEAR FULL TIME – SEPTEMBER START, 16 MONTHS FULL TIME – JANUARY START, (10 STUDENTS)
DEADLINE: 15TH JANUARY (BA COURSES)
Successful, innovative and modern – welcome to the University of

Huddersfield. Whatever you aim to do in life, it pays to get a good education. And with high standards of teaching and learning and excellent facilities that's exactly what our students can expect from the University of Huddersfield. Spread over three campuses in Huddersfield, Oldham and Barnsley we help thousands of people, from school leavers to those returning to education after a gap, achieve their goals each year.

UNIVERSITY OF HULL

HULL HU6 7R
TEL: 01482 346 311
ADMISSIONS@HULL.AC.UK
WWW.HULL.AC.UK
SJP MEMBERS: **270**
COURSES: BA (HONS) MUSIC AND THEATRE, 3 YEARS
BA (HONS) DRAMA AND THEATRE PRACTICE, 3 YEARS
BA (HONS) DRAMA AND ENGLISH, 3 YEARS
BA (HONS) THEATRE AND PERFORMANCE, 3 YEARS
DEADLINE: 15TH JANUARY

For 50 years, as one of the first British Universities to offer Drama, the Drama department at Hull has played a significant part in developing the academic study of the dramatic form as well as producing graduates who are practically aware and have the necessary skills to be employed in theatre. Over 70% of our graduates go on to careers in the creative industries (Theatre, Television, Radio, Film, Events, Journalism, Arts Education and Management) whilst others use the transferable skills gained to begin careers in other areas including law, advertising, education, hospitality and retail management. The department is committed to developing the employability of graduates by keeping our students up-to-date with professional practice and as such we have close ties with theatres in the region including Hull Truck Theatre and West Yorkshire Playhouse. Many of our staff are engaged in projects with regional theatres and theatre companies across the country. There are regular visits to theatres (both performances and general visits) and our graduates from their respective fields often return to the department to talk about their experiences working in the creative industries to the benefit and enlightenment of our current students. We like to think that once you are a member of our department, you will always be a member of our department.

UNIVERSITY OF KENT

THE REGISTRY, CANTERBURY
KENT CT2 7NZ
TEL: 01227 764 000
INFORMATION@KENT.AC.UK
WWW.KENT.AC.UK
SJP MEMBERS: **192**
COURSES: BA (HONS) DRAMA AND THEATRE STUDIES, 3 YEARS, (120-160 STUDENTS)
DEADLINE: 15TH JANUARY

Here are five good reasons to study Drama and Theatre Studies at Kent: Ranked 11th in the UK for Drama, Dance & Cinematics in the 2013 Times Good University Guide; Ranked 13th in the UK for Drama, Dance & Cinematics in the 2013 Guardian University Guide; Ranked 8th in the UK for graduate employment in the Performing Arts in the 2012 Sunday Times University Guide; Ranked as one of the two best departments by the RAE 2008 for 'research power', i.e. for the quality of our research at a world-leading level. Our Jarman building won a prestigious RIBA (Royal Institute of British Architects) Award in May 2010 Our wide range of single and joint honours programmes include an extensive variety of options and a focus on professional practice. You can choose a year abroad, a year in industry or our unique MDrama degree with a pre-professional year that lets you specialise in one aspect of performance, directing, producing or designing.

UNIVERSITY OF LEEDS
LEEDS LS2 9JT
TEL: 0113 243 1751
ENQUIRIES-PCI@LEEDS.AC.UK
WWW.LEEDS.AC.UK
SJP MEMBERS: **355**
COURSES: BA (HONS) PERFORMANCE DESIGN, 3 YEARS
BA (HONS) THEATRE AND PERFORMANCE , 3 YEARS
BA MANAGING PERFORMANCE, 3 YEARS
BA ENGLISH LITERATURE AND THEATRE STUDIES, 3 YEARS
MA WRITING FOR PERFORMANCE AND PUBLICATION, 1 YEAR
DEADLINE: 15TH JANUARY (BA COURSES)

Established in 1904, the University of Leeds is one of the largest higher education institutions in the UK. Leeds is also one of the UK's top ten research institutions and well known throughout the world for its quality of teaching and research. Integrating research with learning and teaching is at the heart of the Leeds strategy; courses are taught by staff engaged in world-class research and cutting-edge professional practice, and teaching programmes are underpinned by this research. Because of this, students at all levels have the opportunity to learn about the research process and experience how knowledge is created. The University has a vision to create, advance and disseminate knowledge, which not only develops outstanding graduates and scholars, but also has a direct impact on global society.

Testimonial about University of Leeds by David Horner:

"Great university with good facilities and friendly, knowledgeable tutors."

Training

University of Lincoln

Brayford Pool
Lincoln LN6 7TS
Tel: 01522 88664
KSLY@LINCOLN.AC.UK
WWW.LINCOLN.AC.UK
SJP MEMBERS: **111**
Courses: BA (Hons) Dance and Drama, 3 years
BA (Hons) Drama, 3 years
Deadline: 15th January

At Lincoln, you will be taught by academic staff with extensive industry experience, many of whom are leading experts in their field. You will also have the chance to work collaboratively alongside them thanks to Lincoln's Student as Producer initiative. We are at the forefront of this growing movement to engage with students directly in all aspects of their teaching and learning. Added to that, the University of Lincoln has enjoyed a meteoric rise up the university league tables and is rated in the top ten nationally for student satisfaction for many of its courses. Over the last decade, we have invested more than £140 million in a state-of-the-art learning environment and excellent facilities. The combination of a vibrant city centre with a range of cultural activities and venues makes Lincoln a fantastic environment in which to live and study.

University of Plymouth

Roland Levinsky Building
Plymouth University
Drake Circus, Plymouth
Devon PL4 8AA
Tel: 01752 600 600
PROSPECTUS@PLYMOUTH.AC.UK
WWW.PLYMOUTH.AC.UK
SJP MEMBERS: **133**
Courses: BA (Hons) Theatre and Performance, 3 years
MRes Theatre and Performance, 1 year
Deadline: 15th January

At Plymouth we offer a range of exciting and rewarding undergraduate, postgraduate and research programmes. All Theatre, Dance & Performing Arts courses at Plymouth University are deeply informed by the research, scholarship, training and creative practice of our staff members.

Testimonial about University of Lincoln by Steven Staff:

"I have been extremely satisfied with the course so far. There are a wide range of subjects covered and each of them is dealt with carefully and in depth. The staff are all very helpful and knowledgeable and there are always opportunities being offered to students so that they can gain more experience in the field. I would recommend this course to anybody."

UNIVERSITY OF SHEFFIELD
WESTERN BANK
SHEFFIELD S10 2TN
TEL: 0114 222 2000
SHEFAPPLY@SHEFFIELD.AC.UK
WWW.SHEF.AC.UK
SJP MEMBERS: **121**
COURSES: BA (HONS) THEATRE AND
PERFORMANCE, 3 YEARS
BA (HONS) ENGLISH AND THEATRE STUDIES, 3
YEARS
MA THEATRE AND PERFORMANCE STUDIES, 1 YEAR
DEADLINE: 15TH JANUARY (BA COURSES)
We are one of the UK's leading
Universities. We were named UK
University of the Year in the 2011 Times
Higher Education Awards. We've
produced five Nobel Prize winners, and
many of our alumni have gone on to
hold positions of great responsibility and
influence around the world.

UNIVERSITY OF WARWICK
COVENTRY CV4 7AL
TEL: 024 7652 3523
ENQUIRIES@WBS.AC.UK
WWW.WARWICK.AC.UK
SJP MEMBERS: **145**
COURSES: BA THEATRE AND PERFORMANCE
STUDIES, 3 YEARS
BA ENGLISH AND THEATRE STUDIES, 3 YEARS
DEADLINE: 15TH JANUARY (BA COURSE)
Warwick is a unique, and uniquely
successful, institution. Despite its relative
youth – it was founded in the mid-1960s
– it is now one of the UK's leading univer-
sities, with an acknowledged reputation

for excellence in research and teaching.
Our research in theatre and performance
is classed as internationally significant and
we are consistently ranked in national
newspapers as one of the very top
departments in the UK. Our options and
core courses are taught by acknowledged
experts in their fields, with particular areas
of interest in theatre and performance
history and historiography; national and
intercultural theatres and performance
evolving from the city, public events and
experiments with new technologies. We
benefit from a wealth of theatrical activity
within easy reach of the campus. In
particular, the University is home to the
Warwick Arts Centre, which includes two
theatres and offers an exciting programme
of theatre, dance, music, comedy,
literature, films and visual art.

UNIVERSITY OF WINCHESTER
WINCHESTER
SO22 4NR
TEL: 01962 841 515
COURSE.ENQUIRIES@WINCHESTER.AC.UK
WWW.WINCHESTER.AC.UK
SJP MEMBERS: **164**
COURSES: BA (HONS) THEATRE PRODUCTION
(STAGE AND ARTS MANAGEMENT), 3 YEARS FULL-
TIME, 6 YEARS PART-TIME
BA (HONS) DRAMA, 3 YEARS FULL-TIME, 6 YEARS
PART-TIME
MA CULTURAL AND ARTS MANAGEMENT, 1 YEAR
FULL-TIME, 2 YEARS PART-TIME
DEADLINE: 15TH JANUARY (BA COURSES)
The Department of Performing Arts is

lively, creative and exciting. With over 600 students and 26 staff, the Department comprises a range of cognate undergraduate and postgraduate programmes which are characterised by an enquiry into the relationship between theory and practice of contemporary performance in various contexts. Some of our programmes are aimed at the study and practice of the arts as agents for change in communities; others study the processes of creating and performing work as disciplines in themselves. We have two fully equipped performance spaces and have recently moved into the purpose built Performing Arts Studios. We have strong external links with venues and festivals in the city of Winchester and the region, and are developing and expanding our national and international links.

UNIVERSITY OF WEST LONDON

ST MARY'S ROAD
EALING, W5 5RF
TEL: 0800 036 8888
LEARNING.ADVICE@UWL.AC.UK
WWW.UWL.AC.UK
COURSES: BA (HONS) THEATRE PRODUCTION (DESIGN AND MANAGEMENT), 3 YEARS, (20 STUDENTS) DEADLINE: 15TH JANUARY
Welcome to the Ealing School of Art, Design and Media (part of the University of West London). We aim to unlock your creative potential with a flexible approach and inspirational staff. Talented practitioners, with expertise in new media and innovative creative techniques, will prepare you for an adaptable career in the fast-paced arena of contemporary art and design. Located in West London, the hub of the UK's creative and media industries, you'll benefit from invaluable opportunities for career engagement too.

UNIVERSITY OF WOLVERHAMPTON

WULFRUNA STREET
WOLVERHAMPTON WV1 1LY
TEL: 01902 321 000
ENQUIRIES@WLV.AC.UK
WWW.WLV.AC.UK
SJP MEMBERS: **98**
COURSES: FD (ARTS) SOUND PRODUCTION, 2 YEARS
BA (HONS) SOUND PRODUCTION (TOP UP), 2 YEARS
BA (HONS) DRAMA AND FILM STUDIES, 3 YEARS FULL-TIME, 5-6 YEARS PART-TIME
BA (HONS) DRAMA AND CREATIVE PROFESSIONAL WRITING, 3 YEARS FULL-TIME, 5-6 YEARS PART-TIME
BA (HONS) DRAMA AND PERFORMANCE, 3 YEARS FULL-TIME, 5-6 YEARS PART-TIME
BA (HONS) DANCE AND DRAMA, 3 YEARS FULL-TIME, 5-6 YEARS PART-TIME
MA DRAMA, 1 YEAR FULL-TIME, 2 YEARS PART-TIME
DEADLINE: 15TH JANUARY (BA COURSES)
The University is a place of knowledge, innovation and enterprise. We pride ourselves on these three tenets. They underpin our strategies in learning and teaching, in research, and help us to

engage with the business world. That is why we have come to play a vital role in the region's economic and cultural development. Our vision for higher education goes beyond opening minds and widening individual horizons. We want our graduates to be valuable assets to the global economies they will come to serve; businesses come back to us because we provide them with solutions that help them to sustain their future. Our research focuses on aspects of life that affect us all.

WIMBLEDON COLLEGE OF ART
MERTON HALL ROAD
LONDON SW19 3QA
TEL: 020 7514 9641
INFO@WIMBLEDON.ARTS.AC.UK
WWW.WIMBLEDON.ARTS.AC.UK
SJP MEMBERS: **223**
COURSES: BA (HONS) THEATRE AND SCREEN – THEATRE DESIGN, 3 YEARS, (24 STUDENTS)
BA (HONS) THEATRE AND SCREEN – COSTUME DESIGN, 3 YEARS, (24 STUDENTS)
BA (HONS) THEATRE: COSTUME DESIGN, 3 YEARS, (24 STUDENTS)
BA (HONS) THEATRE: COSTUME INTERPRETATION, 3 YEARS, (24 STUDENTS)
BA (HONS) THEATRE AND SCREEN – TECHNICAL ARTS AND SPECIAL EFFECTS, 3 YEARS, (24 STUDENTS)
DEADLINE: 15TH JANUARY
Wimbledon College of Art has a long history as a leading specialist art college in London and we are now established within the University of the Arts London

as the sixth college of the University. The College is committed to providing you with an inspiring, challenging and importantly an enjoyable learning experience to facilitate the skills and knowledge you will need for your future career. We are a subject specific College: this means that our main subject areas – Fine Art and Theatre Design – are broken down into subject specific pathways. These pathways are smaller scaled communities of learning and support that will enable you to build your confidence and enthusiasm firstly within your Pathway, then across the College toward the broader University of the Arts environment. Our aim is to increase your independence and ownership of study so that you can make the right choices when they matter most.

YORK ST. JOHN UNIVERSITY
LORD MAYOR'S WALK
YORK YO31 7EX
TEL: 01904 624 624
ARTSADMIN@YORKSJ.AC.UK
WWW.YORKSJ.AC.UK
SJP MEMBERS: **78**
COURSES: BA (HONS) THEATRE, 3 YEAR FULL-TIME, 5-8 YEARS PART-TIME
MA/PG DIP/PG CERT APPLIED THEATRE, 1 YEAR FULL-TIME, 2 YEARS PART-TIME
DEADLINE: 15TH JANUARY (BA COURSE)
There are many things you will love about York St John University including the interesting, contemporary and relevant courses delivered by enthusi-

astic, expert staff. Recent campus investment of over £75m will provide you with an excellent student experience and a terrific range of well located accommodation. And all of this in the exciting environment that is York – with its heritage, vibrant café/bar culture and nightlife. York St John University awards are distinctive and dynamic. They are designed for you to achieve not only the subject specific skills you will need to enter your chosen profession, but also the life and work skills which we know employers are looking for in today's competitive job market. We have a proud tradition of successful achievement for our students – people who come to us from a wide range of backgrounds.

Chapter 3
Key Organisations

Key Organisations

Starting out in a new industry can be a little overwhelming. Which organisation does what? Who would be the best for you? Do you have to pay to use their services?

We've compiled a list of what we think are the main organisations in the theatre world – from trade unions to the best places to go for additional information on the theatre industry itself.

Unions

ASSOCIATION OF BRITISH THEATRE TECHNICIANS (ABTT)
5 FARRINGDON ROAD
LONDON EC1M 3JB
020 7242 9200
WWW.ABTT.ORG.UK
INFO@ABTT.ORG.UK

The Association of British Theatre Technicians is a charity and a company limited by the guarantee of its members. We campaign on behalf of the theatre industry to ensure legislation is appropriate to the industry's needs, and that regulations are suitably drafted and enforced. We provide a telephone and email enquiry service to help solve safety and technical problems for industry chat and difficult questions. We run training courses for technical and managerial skills; these include the Bronze, Silver and Gold Awards and specialist courses including Pyrotechnics and Risk Management. We produce Sightline, the quarterly industry magazine for technical theatre, with news, reviews, features and Safety Matters. Other publications include the theatre industry's Codes of Practice specific to the industry's needs. We produce the Technical Standards for Places of Entertainment in association with the District Surveyors Association and the Institute of Licensing. We also produced the Model National Conditions. Guidance Notes on specific subjects are published when needed. We organise the annual Theatre Show of backstage and front-of house equipment and supplies. We arrange visits, conferences, forums, lectures and meetings for our members. Trips to interesting theatres and productions are arranged, frequently organised by ABTT NorthNet, the get-together of our members especially those north of Watford. The ABTT is the UK centre of OISTAT (International Organization of Scenographers, Theatre Architects and Technicians).

MEMBERSHIP COSTS:
ASSOCIATE – £65
MEMBER – £65
STUDENT – £20

ASSOCIATION OF LIGHTING DESIGNERS (ALD)

PO Box 955
SOUTHSEA
PO1 9NF
078 1706 0189
WWW.ALD.ORG.UK
OFFICE@ALD.ORG.UK

The Association of Lighting Designers is the professional body representing lighting designers in all fields in the United Kingdom and the rest of the world. It exists to provide a resource and forum for the discussion and development of artistic and creative aims amongst designers from the fields of Theatre, Television, Architecture, Education, Industrial and Corporate Presentation and Manufacturing. A principal purpose of the ALD is to provide a forum for LDs to meet each other, and discuss their art and issues affecting their working lives with their peers. Members meetings take the form of: show briefings, where an LD will discuss the lighting design for a show they have lit with demonstrations in the theatre; product demonstrations by leading man-ufactures; and master classes with leading practitioners. The Directory advertises Professional members to potential employers, ensuring that managements looking for lighting designers will find ALD members first. The Association represents members' interests in most negotiating environ-ments. ALD members sit on the Equity Designers' Committee (the union group that negotiates lighting design fees and contracts with the TMA, SOLT and ITC). The ALD also provides a neutral interme-diary in disputes between lighting designers and managements, offering advice and information based on a wealth of professional experience.

MEMBERSHIP COSTS:
PROFESSIONAL DESIGNER – £75
PROFESSIONAL MEMBER – £75
ASSOCIATE – £40
STUDENT – £25

ASSOCIATION OF SOUND DESIGNERS (ASD)

WWW.ASSOCIATIONOFSOUNDDESIGNERS.COM
ADMIN@ASSOCIATIONOFSOUNDDESIGNERS.COM

The Association of Sound Designers is a professional association representing the interests of sound designers in the UK theatre industry. Our function is to connect the widely dispersed sound design community, to educate and promote high standards, and to foster professionalism between client and designer within the industry.

MEMBERSHIP COSTS:
PROFESSIONAL DESIGNER – £75
PROFESSIONAL MEMBER – £75
STUDENT MEMBER – £30
ASSOCIATE MEMBER – £50

Key Organisations

ASSOCIATION OF STAGE PYROTECHNICIANS (ASP)

WWW.STAGE-PYRO.ORG.UK

WEBMASTER@STAGE-PYRO.ORG.UK

The ASP is a UK administered organisation for people working with stage pyrotechnics. The purpose of the Association is to:

- Formalise a group of like minded technicians, operators and managers who wish to share information and dialogue regarding the safe use of theatrical pyrotechnics in stage, concert and conference environments.
- Promote the safe handling, storage, transport and use of a specified range of theatrical pyrotechnic devices.
- Promote training in the safe and appropriate use of a specified range of theatrical pyrotechnic devices, leading to recognition and certification by the Association.
- Provide a forum service for all members working with stage pyrotechnics.
- Provide a centralised register of operators experience and training.
- Provide a verification service to External Agencies including Local Authority Licensing Departments, Fire Service and Insurance Companies.

MEMBERSHIP COSTS:

FREE VIA A TRAINING COURSE

THE BRITISH PUPPET AND MODEL THEATRE ASSOCIATION

65 KINGSLEY AVENUE, EALING

LONDON W13 OEH

020 8997 8236

WWW.PUPPETGUILD.ORG.UK

PETER@PETERPUPPET.CO.UK

Aims and Objectives:

- To protect and promote the skills of puppetry and Model theatre.
- To improve the standards of puppetry in all its forms.
- To establish a basis of communication between its members, in both Great Britain and all parts of the world.

The Guild holds regular meetings across the United Kingdom at which members can exchange views, gain experience through workshops and watch performances. The Guild issues a monthly newsletter which keeps its members in touch with all that is going on in the world of puppetry. The Guild magazine The Puppet Master is published annually and is free to all members.

MEMBERSHIP COSTS:

FULL ADULT MEMBERSHIP – £18

STUDENT – £15

UNDER 16 – £12

THE BROADCASTING, ENTERTAINMENT, CINEMATOGRAPH AND THEATRE UNION (BECTU)

373-377 CLAPHAM ROAD
LONDON SW9 9BT
020 7346 0900
WWW.BECTU.ORG.UK

BECTU is the independent trade union for those working in broadcasting, film, theatre, entertainment, leisure, interactive media and allied areas. The union represents staff and contract and freelance workers who are based primarily in the United Kingdom.

BECTU provides a wide range of services to its more than 25,000 members, including:

- Negotiating pay, conditions and contracts with employers
- Personal advice and representation for individual members
- Advice and representation on health and safety
- Benefits and services for BECTU members
- A union journal, Stage Screen and Radio, published eight times a year.
- A website designed to improve access to the union's advice and support.

MEMBERSHIP COST:
£120 FOR FIRST YEAR

THE DIRECTOR'S GUILD OF GREAT BRITAIN (DGGB)

STUDIO 24, ROYAL VICTORIA PATRIOTIC BUILDING
JOHN ARCHER WAY
LONDON SW18 3SX
020 8871 1660
WWW.DGGB.ORG
INFO@DGGB.ORG

The Directors Guild Trust and the Directors Guild of Great Britain work together to train, promote and celebrate directors and directing across all media: film, television, theatre, radio, opera, commercials, music videos, corporate film, multimedia and new technology. The Guild hosts events and training, produces and sponsors publications, has a respected public voice on arts and media policy and is a forum for members to meet and share experience and skills. We welcome professional directors in all media, students of directing and associated studies, educational establishments teaching directing in theatre, film and television, corporate members who would like access to our facilities and everyone interested in the art and craft of directing. Membership of the Trust, with advanced booking and discounts to Guild events, newsletter and a range of benefits is open to all; professional directors with two or more paid credits are invited to join the register of the Directors Guild of Great Britain.

MEMBERSHIP COSTS:
ASSOCIATE – £65
PROFESSIONAL (2 OR MORE PROFESSIONAL DIRECTING CREDITS) – £65
STUDENT – £25

Key Organisations

EQUITY

GUILD HOUSE
UPPER ST MARTIN'S LANE
LONDON WC2H 9EG
020 7379 6000
WWW.EQUITY.ORG.UK
INFO@EQUITY.ORG.UK

Equity is the UK trade union for professional performers and creative practitioners. As a leading industry organisation, Equity is known and respected nationally and internationally for the work we do with, and on behalf of, our members working across all areas of the entertainment industry. Equity members form a cultural community that is of major importance to the UK in artistic, social and economic terms and Equity works to support them by negotiating their terms and conditions including fee structures with all kinds of employers and employer's groups. Our 5,000 Student Members are also able to access information and advice to help prepare them for work in the industry. We are a campaigning and organising union and proud of our strong record of taking the things that matter to our members to parliament and other centres of influence. Being part of Equity gives members a voice in these places. Members are at the heart of all the union's activities and by getting involved they drive forward the work of the union.

MEMBERSHIP COSTS:
STUDENT – £16.50
THE NON-STUDENT EQUITY MEMBERSHIP IS DEPENDENT UPON GROSS ANNUAL INCOME, AND RANGES FROM £113 (INCOME LESS THAN £20,000) TO £567+ FOR INCOME OF MORE THAN £50,000.

INSTITUTION OF LIGHTING PROFESSIONALS (ILP)

REGENT HOUSE, REGENT PLACE
RUGBY CV21 2PN
01788 576 492
WWW.THEILP.ORG.UK
INFO@THEILP.ORG.UK

The Institution of Lighting Professionals (ILP) is the UK and Ireland's largest and most influential professional lighting association, dedicated solely to excellence in lighting. Founded in 1924 as the Association of Public Lighting Engineers, the ILP has evolved to include lighting designers, consultants and engineers amongst its 1,500 strong membership. The key purpose of the ILP is to promote excellence in all forms of lighting. This includes interior, exterior, sports, road, flood, emergency, tunnel, security and festive lighting as well as design and consultancy services. The Institution is a registered charity, a limited company and a licensed body of the Engineering Council.

MEMBERSHIP COSTS:
STUDENT – £20
NEW AFFILIATES – £150
RENEWAL OF AFFILIATE MEMBERSHIP – £129
ASSOCIATE MEMBER – £143
MEMBER – £159
FELLOW – £189
APPRENTICES/TRAINEES MAY PAY A REDUCED FEE WHILE TRAINING.
IF YOU HAVE BEEN MADE REDUNDANT, YOU CAN CLAIM FREE MEMBERSHIP FOR ONE YEAR.

NATIONAL ASSOCIATION OF SCREEN MAKE-
UP ARTISTS AND HAIRDRESSERS (NASMAH)
020 8998 7494
WWW.NASMAH.CO.UK
In 1996, six film and television make-up
artists invited 50 of the top make-up artists
and hairdressers in the industry to a
meeting about setting up an association
for hairdressing and make-up professionals. From this meeting NASMAH was
born and a constitution drawn up.
NASMAH was formed to maintain the high
standards of artistry achieved in previous
years and to promote the profile of hair
and make-up professionals in the industry.
MEMBERSHIP COSTS:
FRESHMAN – £30
FULL MEMBER – £48
ASSOCIATE – £48

PLASA
REDOUBT HOUSE, 1 EDWARD ROAD
EASTBOURNE BN23 8AS
01323 524 121
WWW.PLASA.ORG
INFO.EU@PLASA.ORG
PLASA is the lead international
membership body for those who supply
technologies and services to the event,
entertainment and installation industries.
As a pro-active trade association, it looks
after the interests of its members and
seeks to influence business practices and
skills development across the industry.
MEMBERSHIP COSTS:
STUDENT – FREE
INDIVIDUAL – £100

THE SOCIETY OF BRITISH THEATRE
DESIGNERS (SBTD)
LIGHTING DESIGN DEPARTMENT
ROSE BRUFORD COLLEGE OF THEATRE AND
PERFORMANCE
BURNT OAK LANE, SIDCUP
DA15 9DF
020 8308 2674
ADMIN@THEATREDESIGN.CO.UK
WWW.THEATREDESIGN.ORG.UK
The Society of British Theatre Designers is
a professional organisation run by
designers for the benefit of designers. It
was created to benefit theatre designers
and their profession and to explore and
further the role of the designer within
the arts today. The SBTD acts as a hub for
the sharing of information and communication between professional designer
members:
• We are seen as the first point of communication in the UK by the
  International Scenographic community,
  and by International companies
  seeking professional designers.
• We provide important industry related
  information for our members and
  promote their work through our
  website.
• We publish a quarterly newsletter, and
  send out regular E-updates by email.
• We provide Directories of suppliers
  including model supplies, armourers,
  costume hire etc.
• We provide Guides for including, Tax,
  Agents, Finding Work, Contracts etc.
• We publish the work, contact details

and biographies of our members on our website.

• We organise training and seminars.

MEMBERSHIP COSTS:

STUDENT – £25

GRADUATE – £35

ASSOCIATE – £35

PROFESSIONAL – £60

THE STAGE MANAGEMENT ASSOCIATION (SMA)

FIRST FLOOR
89 BOROUGH HIGH STREET
LONDON SE1 1NL
020 7403 7999
ADMIN@STAGEMANAGEMENTASSOCIATION.CO.UK

WWW.STAGEMANAGEMENTASSOCIATION.CO.UK

The SMA is the trade association for stage managers, providing advocacy and support. The SMA speaks up on behalf of stage managers, taking stage management issues to other bodies and organisations within the industry and beyond to find appropriate solutions. The SMA provides training, information resources, a quarterly magazine, advice and helplines, mentoring and career development.

MEMBERSHIP COSTS:

PROFESSIONAL – £95

GRADUATE – £42.50 (6 MONTHS)

STUDENT – £25

ASSOCIATE/FRIEND – £40

Other useful organisations

IDEASTAP

WOOLYARD
54 BERMONDSEY STREET
LONDON SE1 3UD
WWW.IDEASTAP.COM
INFO@IDEASTAP.COM

IdeasTap is an arts charity set up to help young, creative people at the start of their careers. Whether it's funding, career development, advice or creative collaborators you need, we can help – whatever field you work in. We've partnered with some major arts organisations and we try to bring our members some incredible exclusive opportunities. Did we mention that membership is free?

STAGE TECHNOLOGIES

STAGE TECHNOLOGIES LIMITED
9 FALCON PARK
NEASDEN LANE
LONDON
NW10 1RZ
020 8208 6000
WWW.STAGETECH.COM

A long-term promoter of stage engineering in the world of performance, Stage Technologies has evolved hand-in-hand with and been a key developer of this exciting market. On more than one occasion, we have been the only theatre automation supplier capable of delivering a complex brief and we have helped realise many industry firsts and defining moments in live entertainment history since our inception in 1994. We are now a global organisation with projects in over 30 countries, encompassing a worldwide network driven by offices in London, Las Vegas, Macau, Hong Kong, and Australia.

THE THEATRICAL GUILD (TTG)
11 GARRICK STREET
LONDON WC2E 9AR
020 7240 6062
WWW.TTG.ORG.UK
ADMIN@TTG.ORG.UK

The Theatrical Guild was established to support people in the theatrical profession who are in need. We offer advice; financial support towards equipment, bills or specialist health care appointments; as well as funds towards the cost of education or retraining. Typically people that come to us have had an accident, are ill or are unable to work for a number of reasons. You may be able to receive support if you are suffering due to an emergency. Our aim is to try to help you solve the immediate problem and empower you to find longer term solutions or get back to work (if applicable). We often give out one off grants but can support people on an ongoing basis.

GET INTO THEATRE
020 7015 1840
WWW.GETINTOTHEATRE.ORG

Get Into Theatre is all about working in the theatre. This site hopes to open your eyes to the huge variety of careers in the industry – and the different ways to get there. At Get Into Theatre you can read interviews with people who are already working in theatre – onstage, backstage and offstage – and discover over 80 careers in theatre. You can also hold up your hand and ask our expert panel a question. If you're feeling active, you can find out about applying for work experience or check out some current work experience placements – we even list some paid jobs in theatre. You can discover local theatres and theatre companies, explore your education options at 14, 16, 18 and above, or you can go back to basics and read our overview of the theatre industry.

Key Organisations

CREATIVE CHOICES

WWW.CREATIVE-CHOICES.CO.UK

INFO@CREATIVE-CHOICES.CO.UK

Creative Choices is managed by Creative & Cultural Skills, as part of our mission to enable the creative and cultural industries to achieve their economic potential through skills and training. We founded Creative Choices following a demand from employers across the creative sector for better, and more representative, information about working in the industry. The purpose of the website is to be a resource for the creative and cultural industries, created and endorsed by the sector. Our aim is to offer clear and accessible information, advice and guidance to individuals throughout their careers, helping you to build skills, find new opportunities, or get a better idea about a particular job or career path.

CREATIVE & CULTURAL SKILLS

LAFONE HOUSE

THE LEATHERMARKET

WESTON STREET

LONDON SE1 3HN

020 7015 1800

WWW.CCSKILLS.ORG.UK

Creative & Cultural Skills is the licensed Sector Skills Council for the UK's creative and cultural industries, including craft, cultural heritage, design, literature, music, performing arts and visual arts. Our goal is to enable the creative and cultural industries to reach their economic potential through relevant skills and training. We work in England, Northern Ireland, Scotland and Wales and with international partners.

Our work includes:

- Supporting the creative sector to take on apprentices through our Creative Apprenticeships programme
- Providing information, advice and guidance for creative careers through our Creative Choices programme
- Providing research and analysis in to the skills needs of the industry through our Creative Blueprint programme
- Supporting the creative sector to set the standards for high-quality work in the industry through our Professional Standards programme
- Providing specialist rehearsal space and training for the live music and theatre industries at The Backstage Centre in Purfleet, Essex.

NATIONAL SKILLS ACADEMY

LAFONE HOUSE

THE LEATHERMARKET

WESTON STREET

LONDON SE1 3HN

020 7015 1840

WWW.NSA-CCSKILLS.CO.UK

NSA@CCSKILLS.ORG.UK

We are a membership network of 20 colleges and 220 theatre and live music employers nationwide. We recognise, develop and improve skills opportunities to help you get into our industry and get on in it once you're there. We create industry-endorsed careers advice and guidance through our annual careers events and online resources. We promote entry routes and apprenticeships within the creative and cultural sector, through our Apprenticeship Training Service. We work with our Founder College network and specialist training providers to promote training and professional development for those already working within the sector.

DRAMAUK

WWW.DRAMAUK.CO.UK

Drama UK is the new body championing quality drama training in the UK, formed from the merging of CDS and the NCDT. Drama UK will continue to fulfil the functions of CDS and NCDT including offering advice on professional training and accreditation of vocational courses. Drama UK will also provide support to those organisations offering accredited training. At the same time it will act as an advocate for the sector, championing excellence in drama training and encouraging the industry and training providers to continue to work together.

DISABILITY ARTS ONLINE

9 JEW STREET
BRIGHTON BN1 1UT
07411 824458
WWW.DISABILITYARTSONLINE.ORG.UK
INFO@DISABILITYARTSONLINE.ORG.UK

Disability Arts Online is a repository of thousands of articles: blogs, news items, reviews, interviews, galleries and creative writing by artists and writers, writing on disability and the arts, which have been published since 2004. Edited by disabled artist Colin Hambrook, DAO is a unique journal for discussion of arts and culture, giving disabled and deaf artists, performers, film-makers, writers, and critics a place to talk about and share artistic practice.

Chapter 4
Applying for Jobs

Applying for Jobs

These days applying for jobs, and even work experience and internships, is extremely competitive. There are more and more people looking for employment, and fewer and fewer opportunities out there.

Whether you're applying for your first job or your 50th, or if you're simply contacting a local theatre to ask if you can come in and help, it's important that you present yourself in the best possible light to improve your chances of success.

Here is our guide to contacting people in the industry, developing your contacts and landing that job of your dreams.

Your CV

Your CV is your means of getting someone's attention and showcasing your great skills and experience. A great CV can get you in the door fast, a bad CV can end up in the bin.

DO...
- Make your CV clear and well organised. The person reading it may be looking through hundreds of CVs – make yours concise and easy to read.
- Check, and then check again, for spelling, grammar and formatting mistakes.
- Be selective: highlight your best achievements, and don't feel that you have to include a mini essay for every point. You can discuss them in your interview.
- If you have an interesting hobby or pastime, include it! It sets you apart from others, makes a great talking point in the interview and shows you are a well-rounded individual.
- Make your CV professional – if you're using colours, use a very restrained colour scheme, use one simple font throughout (not Curlz MT) and do not use clip-art. Do vary the font size – e.g. name in large letters at top of page, section headings in a large-ish size, content in a smaller size – but again, keep it to two or three sizes. Any more, and the document will look messy and unprofessional.
- Don't assume that zany = good. There's a lot of information about

'creative' CVs online – people sending t-shirts with their CVs printed on them, or creating magazines or games with their CVs in them. However, you have to be very careful with this – a lot of the most unconventional CVs are related to design or marketing jobs. If you're applying for Box Office Manager or Sound Technician, it's probably better to go with a standard CV.

- Use bullet points, headings, paragraphs, and page-breaks to break up your CV. This will make it easier to look at and read.
- Try not to use online templates or word processor templates. If you do use a template, change it – alter the colour scheme, reverse the order of some sections, or change font sizes.
- Organise it sensibly – for example, if listing GCSEs do them in alphabetical order or if you are listing your previous jobs, do them in chronological order.
- Use the job advert to help shape your CV – make clear how you fulfil the criteria they have given. Use the same vocabulary and terms that they do in the advert.
- Be careful with formatting. Email your CV as a PDF, so as to ensure that the recipient does not just end up with an incoherent jumble if they open it in a different version of Word!
- Keep updating your CV. You will never have a perfect, definitive CV. As you do more work, change career direction, move country, or just apply for different jobs, you will have to change your CV. Do this often, rather than risking the sudden realisation that the CV you've been handing out is three years out of date.

DON'T
- Try and avoid cliche – employers are looking for a CV that stands out, rather than another person who is 'a very good team player' or 'excellent problem-solver'. On the other hand, don't go crazy – you need to make clear that you can write appropriately.
- Don't send the same CV out to everyone. Depending on the job you're applying for, you'll have to modify your CV – for a young, hip, quirky theatre company, you might want to do something more cheerful than for a well-established and prestigious theatre company, and similarly for different roles you might want to

highlight different experience and qualifications. Make your CV relevant to the job.

- Don't put in EVERYTHING THAT YOU HAVE EVER DONE. Two pages is long enough, one is even better – any more than that and it may not get read.
- Don't title it Curriculum Vitae or CV. That should be obvious without a title.
- Don't use long words to show how clever you are – use appropriate vocabulary. If you made the props for a play, it's not going to help to say that you 'fabricated the theatrical properties for a stage production'.
- Don't just list your previous jobs. Include a short sentence about what you've achieved, not just what you've done – explain how you improved something or developed a skill.
- Don't include a photograph of yourself. Some visual roles, Costume / Lighting Designer or Make-up Artist, may require a portfolio.
- Perhaps most importantly: NEVER be tempted to lie or stretch the truth about your abilities – you will get found out. Also, the theatre industry is a remarkably small world – you may find that, having lied to one company, everyone suddenly seems hesitant to hire you.

There's lots more information about CVs online - searching 'CV' on The Guardian website, for example, brings up lots of useful articles.

Covering Letters & Contacting People

Whether you're applying for a job or simply contacting a local theatre for work experience, there are some golden rules to follow to ensure you get the best possible response:

- DON'T send the same letter and CV to lots of companies – personalise them. Why are you contacting them specifically? Tell them why you like their work, or if you saw their production recently, tell them what you liked about it for instant brownie points.
- DO check your letter/email and CV obsessively and in great detail. An application for the post of 'Assitant Director' or 'Choreographer'

won't stand you in good stead. Don't rely solely on spellcheck – their/they're and your/you're errors won't be picked up.

- DON'T just repeat what you've already written in your CV. You can bring out the most important details, so as to encourage them to take a look at your CV, but don't just write a summary of your CV. Take advantage of the opportunity to personalise your application.
- DO keep it concise. Two or three paragraphs is enough – any more, and they won't bother to read it.
- DON'T apply at the last minute – if you send your email two hours before the deadline, it suggests to the employer that you are disorganised, and don't care enough about this job to make the effort to prepare.
- DO use an appropriate tone. Keep it formal – if you know the name of the person you're writing to (and do try to find this out), then refer to them by their title and last name (Mr. Jones, Dr. Smith), rather than by their first name. Even if they are the 'Call me Joe' type, they're not going to be offended by you being slightly too formal in the first instance, but might be by an over-familiar 'Hi Joe!'.
- DO write in the first person singular – 'I am', 'I have', 'I would like'. Writing about yourself in the third person ('John is', 'John would like') just makes you sound slightly strange.
- DON'T be tempted to get your parents to write/call for you – if you're mature enough to apply for and hold down a job, you're mature enough to take control yourself. This doesn't mean you can't ask your parents to help you with proofreading your CV and cover letter – just make sure that you're the one who contacts the company.

Email Etiquette

Sometimes it's hard to know whether to contact a company or a theatre by email or letter – lots of our members recommend a dual-pronged attack by email and post. If you're sending a letter by post, however, do make the effort to find out the name of the right person to address it to – call the company and ask if you're not sure.

There are some general pitfalls to avoid when contacting someone by email:

- Check your spelling and grammar – it can be tempting to just fire off a quick email, but it's just as easy for the person at the other end to press 'delete'.
- Get yourself a professional email address – yourname@email.com or similar tends to work best.
- Personalise Personalise Personalise – people can see copied and pasted emails coming a mile off, and doing so can mean that errors involving the wrong names start to creep in.

Your Online Presence

Leading on from emails, it's important to be aware of your presence on the internet and understand what this can say about you to a potential employer. Employers can see a lot of what you post online under your name – your Facebook profile pictures, your Twitter account, your blog – and they will look you up when you apply for a job.

Because of this, it is very important to monitor and construct your online profiles carefully – pictures of you dancing the macarena with a bottle of cider in each hand may show how fun and bubbly you are, but they are unlikely to appeal to anyone thinking of hiring you.

It is also necessary to be cautious with all forms of social media – saying 'was just interviewed by bunch of idiots for a stupid job' or 'applying for reeeeeeeeeally booooooooring job' on Twitter is not likely to enhance your chances of getting the job, even if your Facebook profile is squeaky clean.

That's not to say that the internet can't be useful – maintaining a profile on websites like Stage Jobs Pro or LinkedIn can allow people to find out more about you before hiring you, and can allow people to network easily. Lots of employer actively seek people who understand and actively use social media – it's becoming an increasingly important skill in the workplace. However, do be very careful with what you post online, and make sure that you only post things you wouldn't mind an employer seeing.

Ambassador Theatre Group HR Department – Applying for Jobs

THIS GUIDE WAS KINDLY WRITTEN BY THE HR DEPARTMENT AT AMBASSADOR THEATRE GROUP

Make sure your application is well presented

Your CV or application form is your first introduction to your prospective employer and first impressions count. Grammar, punctuation and spelling are still enormously important in creating a good first impression and presentation is key. Check, recheck and read again before you send your form off or get someone else to look through it with fresh eyes. A good application will be remembered even if you don't necessarily have the right skills we're looking for at the time. If the format of the form is an issue for you, tell us. Better that we find a way around it than think you haven't tried.

Double check the application details

If we've asked you to complete an application form, don't send in your CV. Likewise, please don't put on your application form, please see CV... if an application form is requested, then it's part of the application process.

Make sure all information is relevant

We receive a number of actor CVs with pictures and vital statistics, but listing all your acting credits doesn't show us why you are the ideal candidate for, for example, a marketing role. Make sure you carefully read the job description and person specification and show us what skills and experiences you have that are relevant to the role.

Sell yourself

Tell us why you are interested in the job you are applying for and what you can bring to the role. Fill in as much of the application form as you possibly can. Don't leave the supporting statement blank. Supporting information is your opportunity to tell

"A good application will be remembered even if you don't necessarily have the right skills we're looking for at the time"

189

us why you are right for the role. Even if you think you might not have the skills and experience you imagine we are looking for, consider what skills and experiences you do have that could be relevant and transferable and tell us why you might be suitable.

Do your research

Send your application to the contact specified in the advert, and spell their name correctly. If you're sending in a speculative application, make sure the role you put yourself forward for is potentially available at the theatre. As an example, we get a lot of applications for wardrobe departments across the country, but virtually all our theatres are receiving houses meaning we don't operate with that department.

This guide was kindly written by the HR Department at Ambassador Theatre Group. ATG has to date employed well over a thousand Stage Jobs Pro members and you can find out more about their theatres at **www.atgtickets.com**

Your Contacts

Make use of any contacts you have – family, university alumni, school teachers, or people you've worked with before. Your school drama teacher may know someone in a theatre company who could organise work experience for you, or you may know someone (or more likely, someone who knows someone who knows someone who knows someone) who could help you out – if it helps you get into theatre, use it.

Networking is very important in theatre – use your contacts from productions you've been involved in (or use their contacts) to get in touch with people who you would be interested in working with or for. Also, make sure you consistently work well as someone in the crew might mention you to someone else for another production. Theatre is an industry built on personal recommendations – make sure your name is the first mentioned.

Interview Technique

Whether you're applying for work experience or jobs, you'll probably have to attend an interview. You've done all the hard work by this point, but there are still some simple things to keep in mind once you've got your foot in the door to keep it there!

How to prepare

Write practice questions and model answers. Go through all the standard questions (a lot of which are online) – tell me about yourself, what are your strengths, what are your weaknesses, why do you want this job, why do you want to work here, give an example of when you have shown leadership and so on.

Do practice interviews (using your questions and answers) with family, friends, or, even better, someone in a similar role or field to the person who will be interviewing you.

Research the company extensively. Don't just look at the front page of their website as everyone will have done that. Look in greater detail – find out about the director, the company, the production, and other productions the director has undertaken. If there are company 'principles' or 'aims', find out what they are, and figure out how you fit in with them. Look up the company's previous work, and be ready to talk about this. If you have any connections with the theatre or theatre company, ask your contact questions about working there, and do not be afraid to drop this into your conversation – it'll put across that you're genuinely enthusiastic, to the extent that you went out and asked someone about the company.

If possible, look up the person who is interviewing you. If you're well-informed about the company and have an idea of who will be inter-viewing you, you'll feel better prepared.

Dress appropriately. Again, this will vary depending on where you are applying, who is interviewing you and so on, but generally the rules are:

- Smart and sensible clothing
- All visible unusual piercings taken out
- Any visible tattoos covered (within reason).

Know your CV – it won't reflect well on you if you can't answer a question which is based on your CV, or if you contradict your CV.

If it's widely available, read the play or script if you're going to be working on a specific production, and be prepared to talk about it.

If the interviewer asks an unexpected question, or you can't answer their question – DON'T PANIC. Take a moment to think about it – it is much better to think for a moment, and give a coherent answer, than babble nonsense immediately. If you need the question clarified or rephrased, ask for this – once more, it is much better to ask for clarification than to talk rubbish.

Be polite, respectful, and appropriate – the interviewer wants someone who can communicate appropriately in a given situation.

GET THERE ON TIME. Aim to be there at least 15 minutes early – if you get there an hour early, you can always have a coffee nearby, while you go over your CV. Make sure you have the company's number, so that if you are going to be late you can call ahead. If you are late, apologise.

During the interview, be aware of how you're sitting and moving. If you fiddle or tap through the whole interview, the interviewer may get irritated and find it difficult to focus on what you're saying. If you're clutching the arm-rests of your seat for dear life, you'll seem very nervous, but equally, if you're slouched in your chair and poking stuff on the interviewer's desk, you'll seem too relaxed, suggesting that you either don't care or don't understand what behaviour is appropriate in a given situation.

At the end of most interviews, you'll be asked if you have any questions. Make sure to always have a question, to show that you have a genuine interest in the company or job. Often it's best to go with things you are genuinely interested in finding out the answer to, but make sure that the question is not something that you could have found out from their website if you'd just looked, and that the question is professional and appropriate.

Relax. While you may be panicking about the interview, that's not the impression you want to give the interviewer, as being remembered as 'the frightened one' is not preferable. The objective is to have a conversation with the interviewer, answer any questions that they have about you, give them an idea of who you are, and, cliched as it sounds, build a relationship. If you are well prepared and have arrived in good time, you'll feel more relaxed. Be polite, pleasant, and calm, and you should be fine.

Thank the interviewer at the end, and, either that day or the next, send them an email saying thank you. Keep the email short, and use it to mention anything you didn't manage to mention in the interview, reiterate anything you want them to remember, and restate your interest in the job, possibly in relation to something the interviewer mentioned. Try not to be heavy-handed, as you want this to come across as a thank you letter which happens to have a few points about how interesting you and the job are, rather than an attempt to save a failed interview. Once more, check the email very, very thoroughly.

If you're called for an interview but find you are unable to attend make sure that you contact the company / interviewer to make your apologies, and possibly arrange an alternative time for interview. Simply not turning up is wasting their time, representing you in a bad light, and cutting off any future contact between you and the employer.

Try not to worry if you don't get the job – there is a lot of competition in the theatre industry. Being asked for interview or a chat proves you're very much on the right track. Contact your interviewer, and ask them if they'd be willing to give you feedback on the interview. Sometimes it is appropriate to send a message thanking the company for the interview and asking them to keep your details on file should a position arise in the future.

If you don't get the job, keep busy. Do some voluntary work for local theatre companies, your school, or local amateur dramatics groups. Three months spent surfing the internet and watching The Jeremy Kyle Show does not look good to employers. Three months taking part in a few productions and gaining experience, does.

Where to Find Jobs

 Stage Jobs Pro – we are the UK's central directory for theatre professionals with 100s of theatre jobs every month
www.stagejobspro.com/uk

The Stage newspaper is published once a week and has a job listings section **www.thestage.co.uk**

Get Into Theatre has a Jobs Board **www.getintotheatre.org/jobs**

The Guardian website lists Theatre Jobs **www.guardian.co.uk/jobs**

The Blue Room is a technical forum which regularly lists jobs
www.blue-room.org.uk

IdeasTap also has a Jobs Board
www.ideastap.com/Opportunities/Jobs

The Arts Council runs a free jobs mailing list service:www.artsjobs.org.uk

Arts Hub **www.artshub.co.uk/uk**

Artsjobsonline
www.artsjobsonline.com

Chapter 5
The Theatre Industry

The following are a selection of guides on various key elements of the industry.

Arts Funding

Putting on productions costs money. Lots of it. Hiring a performance space, costumes, props, and paying a cast and crew can be very expensive. Luckily there is arts funding out there to help – particularly if you're doing work that is innovative, groundbreaking, aims to be inclusive to minority groups, or which tackles a topical or social issue. Here's our basic rundown of which organisations can help and the right way to approach a funding application.

Arts Funding Organisations

The Arts Council (which has separate departments for Wales, Scotland, Northern Ireland, and England) is an organisation that receives government funding and money from The National Lottery, and then invests it into art-related projects – dance, theatre, music, art, and many other forms. You can apply for funding at **www.artscouncil.org.uk/funding/apply-for-funding**.

IdeasTap is a not-for-profit creative funding organisation, that was set up to help fund young people in the arts at the start of their careers. They offer funding for arts projects themselves, but also have a very informative section on Arts Funding at **www.ideastap.com/Funding**

The **BBC Performing Arts Fund** provides financial and other support to individuals and groups who would otherwise not be able to perform. More information can be found at **www.bbc.co.uk/performingartsfund**.

Deborah Williams: Applying to ACE

THIS ARTICLE HAS BEEN REPRODUCED IN ITS ENTIRETY WITH KIND PERMISSION FROM INTERVIEWER AMELIA FORSBROOK AND IDEASTAP

Applying for public funding can be an intimidating and competitive process, but you won't have much luck if you give up at the first hurdle. Deborah Williams, a Relationship Manager in the London theatre team at Arts Council England, reveals the efforts her team go to support and facilitate creativity, and explains why you should apply...

At Arts Council England we advocate, develop and invest. We have "Achieving great art for everyone" as our 10-year strategic plan and our priorities are around excellence and engagement, enabling artists to create great work and ensuring everyone has access to fantastic artistic experiences. We're also creating things with digital in mind. Digital and the creative economy are areas that are quite new to the Arts Council so we're learning from the sector in some ways.

Essentially, I have two parts to my role. One is to work with National Portfolio Organisations, supporting them and putting together a funding agreement to help them to achieve our joint aims; the other side is working on Grants for the Arts. Here, I am part of panels that make recommendations on what projects to support. I also offer advice to potential applicants who come to us with enquiries. I'm a writer and performer as well and was once in the same position, thinking, "I have no idea what I'm doing, but I want to do this – and I'm going to!"

I don't think enough people aged 18, 19 or 20 submit applications. Get on our radar. Go to networking events and conferences, pick out a list of people from the Arts Council you would like to meet and introduce yourself so that we know who you are and we get an idea of what kind of projects you might be doing. I think it's good for us to be able to respond to what the sector is doing. We encourage conversations to take place to make sure people are heading in the right direction. This means that when applications come in, the knowledge is a shared knowledge and people don't have to try too hard to be seen and heard.

Sit down and take the time to figure the application process out. When you're trying something for the first time, it is going to be daunting. Find all the information you can on our website and if you find you need a little bit more

"Create networks and work with people who are happy to support you"

support, you can ask specific questions. We want to make sure that as many people as possible are submitting good applications that best represent what they're trying to do and achieve.

It's great if you've got friends who have a particular kind of experience. Create networks and work with people who are happy to support you. If you are the artist and the focus of the project, then great, but if you can't do the producing or the accounting, find people who can. This will enable you to deliver the work to the standard and the quality that you want to deliver it to.

Top tips:

- Look at the Grants for the Arts web page to familiarise yourself with Arts Council's priorities
- Balance your books. Your income and your expenditure need to be the same.
- Request feedback if you need it. Deborah admits that her colleagues haven't as much time as they'd like to dedicate to this, but they can offer "a phone call, an email, or possibly a meeting."
- Your project may be great, but applying for Arts Council funding is a competitive process. Prepare to think about how you can improve and resubmit your proposal if it is unsuccessful.
- You don't have to come with a finished product. Grants for the Arts is also available for research and development work. The Arts Council acknowledges that creativity takes time to grow.

This article has been reproduced in its entirety with kind permission from interviewer Amelia Forsbrook and IdeasTap. IdeasTap is an arts charity set up to help young, creative people at the start of their careers, you can find out more and join at **www.ideastap.com**. You can check out Amelia's profile on Ideastap here: **www.ideastap.com/People/ ameliaforsbrook**

Other Funding Options

For smaller projects it is also possible to fundraise independently. In recent years, crowd-funding websites such as IndieGoGo, Kickstarter, and RocketHub have become very successful, allowing people to raise money online. Good marketing is essential if funding your production in this way – what makes your work worth investing in? What can you do to encourage people to donate – could you make videos, or reward people for donating? How could you use social media to help spread the word? Making your company and production look as professional as possible will give people the confidence to part with their hard-earned cash.

It's also possible to fundraise in the real world – for example, by holding special events such as concerts and charging for entry. This method of fundraising often depends on your ability to pitch your project to people, and is usually more effective if people are personally approached, rather than being emailed en masse. When raising money independently, it is important to be aware of your fundraising target, and be realistic.

Even if you do have a budget, improvising and being creative to save money are vital skills in the theatre industry – and can actually mean you end up with a more interesting production. Could you use your school's auditorium as a venue? Services such as Freecycle (**uk.freecycle.org**) and Set Exchange (**www.set-exchange.co.uk**) are great ways of getting props and set for free – just make sure you list your items when you're done!

Arts Funding: Useful Links and Websites

Arts Council England:
www.artscouncil.org.uk | 0845 300 6200

Arts Council of Northern Ireland:
www.artscouncil-ni.org | info@artscouncil-ni.org | 028 9038 5200

Arts Council of Wales:
www.artswales.org.uk | 0845 8734 900

Scottish Arts Council:
www.scottisharts.org.uk | help.desk@scottisharts.org.uk | 0131 226 6051

Arts Council Ireland:
www.artscouncil.ie | +353 1618 0200

IdeasTap
www.ideastap.com | info@ideastap.com

BBC Performing Arts Fund
www.bbc.co.uk/performingartsfund

Institute of Fundraising – Introduction to Fundraising
www.institute-of-fundraising.org.uk/guidance/about-fundraising

How 2 Fundraise
www.how2fundraise.org

IndieGoGo
www.indiegogo.com

Kickstarter
www.kickstarter.com

RocketHub
www.rockethub.com

We Fund
wefund.com

Sponsume.com
www.sponsume.com

We Did This
www.peoplefund.it/arts

Set Exchange
www.set-exchange.co.uk

Freecycle
www.uk.freecycle.org/

Gumtree
www.gumtree.com

Arts Festivals & Fringe Theatre

What is Fringe Theatre?

Fringe Theatre is independent, non-mainstream theatre. It is often low-budget and less predictable than larger, mainstream productions. Fringe Theatre as a term encompasses both Fringe venues – small theatres, or places that aren't traditionally performance venues but will host performances anyway such as pubs or cafes – and semi-professional theatre companies.

Fringe Festivals are events where a particular town, city, or region will host lots of Fringe theatre performances within a short space of time. Fringe Festivals are notable for allowing any performers (amateur or professional) to apply with any kind of theatrical content (within reason). Usually the only restriction with Fringe Festivals is that the available venues and performance slots are greatly outnumbered by the applicants, so performers have to be refused due to limitations of space and time.

The main representative of amateur performance in the UK is the National Operatic and Dramatic Association: **www.noda.org.uk**

What are Arts Festivals?

Arts Festivals are similar to Fringe Festivals, in that they are usually a series of performances in various venues in a small area. Unlike Fringe, Arts Festivals can have performances belonging to a variety of disciplines – theatre, dance, poetry, visual arts – or may just specialise in one subject, such as the Brighton Early Music Festival.

The level of performers also varies between festivals – some arts festivals will only have famous, high-calibre performers, and a great deal will be expected from each performance. Other smaller festivals may give amateur musicians/theatre companies/comedians the chance to perform, and some solely focus on young people. Arts festivals can be a great place for small theatre companies to perform but it's important to take the time to find one that's appropriate in terms of experience, genre and budget. An extensive list of arts festivals can be found at **www.artsfestivals.co.uk**.

How does it all work?

When applying to Arts and Fringe Festivals, it's usually necessary to contact the festival organisers and submit an application to perform. However, make sure you check the organiser's website where there will be clear guidelines on the application process – when performing at the Edinburgh Fringe, for example, you apply directly to specific venues. Whoever you're applying to, it's usually worth applying early, as fringe festivals are very popular, and venues can get booked up quite far in advance.

If you want to stage a performance at a fringe venue, you'll need to decide which one and then make contact to negotiate booking costs and other considerations with them directly.

What are the advantages?

Because Fringe Theatre and Arts Festivals are often focused on small scale, non-professional performance, performers have greater scope for unusual, creative performances. They can also potentially attract a much larger audience and more media attention than a company might have had back home. A successful performance at a fringe festival has launched the careers of many performers and theatre companies, and can often lead to UK tours or future performance bookings. They're also a great place to network with other like-minded people in a wonderfully creative and exciting environment, and watch productions and shows you otherwise might not get a chance to see.

Brighton Festival Fringe Guide: How to Fringe – FAQ

THIS ARTICLE HAS BEEN REPRODUCED IN ITS ENTIRETY WITH KIND PERMISSION FROM BRIGHTON FRINGE

What is Brighton Fringe?

B righton Fringe is the largest open-access, multi-art form festival in England. Located in Brighton & Hove, the city has a unique heritage of liberalism and creativity. Brighton Fringe 2013 will take place from 4 May – 2 June.

Brighton Fringe Ltd is a service organisation and registered charity that looks to support and educate artists and producers to promote the arts to a wider audience.

When did it start and why?

Brighton Fringe started as an extension to the Brighton Festival's curated programme in 1967 and worked as a showcase for local artists, performers and promoters. This Brighton Fringe grew so considerably that it became a company and festival in its own right in 2006.

Who can take part?

We neither select nor programme the events that are included so anyone can put on an event as part of the festival.

What if I'm from overseas and a non UK based performer?

Brighton Fringe has recently been granted permit free status and welcomes national and international acts. If you are a performer from outside the UK please be sure to read the Guide for Overseas Participants before you register your event.

What are the benefits of taking part?

- See your event listed in the Brighton Fringe brochure: 100,000 brochures are printed and distributed in Brighton, Sussex and London

- See your event listed on the Brighton Fringe website: with over 200,000 unique visitors during the on-sale period.

- Sell your tickets through the Brighton Fringe Box Office. With over 100,000 tickets sold overall, we'll sell your tickets online, by phone and over the counter, 24 hours a day, 7 days a week.

- Qualify for our bursary scheme and get your registration for free. In 2012, twelve shows by local promoters received a free registration, thanks to the support of Legal & General.

- See that your event gets noticed: With thousands of previews and reviews, the media and online networks covered every angle of Brighton Fringe they could find, both on a local and national scale. Alongside 25 awards presented to Brighton Fringe shows, it's a great opportunity to get your name out there

- Make this an opportunity to showcase your talents, run an event, promote a new show, film, songs, performance, act or skill. With over 180,000 people attending Brighton Fringe events, make sure you get seen.

How can I take part?
Before you start, you'll need to make sure you have the following:

- An event – Your event can be anything you like... a comedy sketch, a musical, an exhibition, an installation, a tour, a film or a book fair

- A venue – Your event can he held anywhere you like... a theatre, a pub, a taxi, a sewer, a park, a tent, a beach hut, a café, or your own house

- A date – Your event can take place at any time between Saturday 4 May-Sunday 2 June 2013; be it a one night show or even better, a 30 day run – it's up to you!

Where is the central hub of Brighton Fringe (e.g. in Edinburgh the Royal Mile)?
For the past few years we have run an outdoor event each Saturday called Fringe City. This takes place in the centre of Brighton around New Road, attracting 40,000 visitors. The event consists of a number of stages and performances where we would not only encourage participants to perform, dress up and parade but flyer too - not unlike the Royal Mile in that sense.

How many tourists does the festival estimate it generates?
Visit Brighton estimates that Brighton saw as many as 1 million visitors during its festival month of May in 2012. Brighton Fringe saw 180,000 attendances in 2012 and sold more than 100,000 tickets.

How many performances or events can I do?
You can register as many events as you like – the more you register, the less each event costs. If you wish to run one event with numerous performances you only pay one price.

How long are the runs at Brighton Fringe?

The length of your run will be determined by your aims and budget for the event, if you are looking to get a review we advise that you do more than one show. A popular formula is to do a few shows in the first week, gain a review and come back for the last week; this will give enough time for word-of-mouth to spread amongst audiences. Of course it is all dependent upon what your personal objectives are and why you are taking part; feel free to talk it over with Participant Services for further advice.

"Brighton Fringe saw 180,000 attendances in 2012 and sold more than 100,000 tickets"

When is the best time to approach venues?

As soon as possible, the sooner the better.

How do I find a venue?

Any space can become a Brighton Fringe venue. To look through already existing Brighton Fringe venues available for hire take a look at the online Venue Directory. This is a searchable directory of all the venues registered to be a part of Brighton Fringe. The directory entries contain contact information and details on hire availability. If you want to register a new space you can do this on the event registration form.

How do I advertise a venue as available for hire?

Download a venue registration form from brightonfringe.org. We'll get all the details of your venue on the online venue directory, and send artists and performers looking for space your way.

When do I register my event?

Registration for Brighton Fringe 2013 will open 23 October 2012.

The final deadline for registration is 4 February 2013. Tickets go on sale mid-February.

How do I register my event?

Once registration opens, you can create a login and start registering your event(s) on the Brighton Fringe website. You register your events one by one and pay at the end. You'll need all the details of your event confirmed, but you needn't complete the form in one go – your login will allow you to complete it section by section.

What is the cost to register?

The cost to register will depend on how many events you are registering, whether you are a charity or school and whether you qualify for the bursary scheme or the early bird discount rate. Prices for 2013 will be published online in October 2012.

What is the bursary scheme and who qualifies for this?

The bursary scheme works on a first come first served basis, and is open to registrants from the Brighton and Hove area. If you have a BN postcode, are running a one event in one of the four categories (Music, Kids & Youth, Literature and Comedy) you may qualify. Please note that if you have been previously awarded a bursary you will not be eligible for one in 2013.

"Brighton Fringe does not invite artists to perform, nor does it produce or pay anyone to be a part of the festival"

What is included in my registration fee?

- Your event listed in the Brighton Fringe brochure and website

- A free Brighton Fringe display board for your venue

- Discounted additional advertising in the brochure and on the website

- A box office service to maximise your ticket sales

- All the help and support you need from our dedicated Brighton Fringe team in the registration, set up and promotion of your event, including free workshops.

- The opportunity to showcase your event at Fringe City – the biggest outdoor event in Brighton during May

- The chance to create your own additional web page on the Brighton Fringe website for free

- Press and publicity – get it previewed, reviewed and awarded because of the media attention Brighton Fringe gets
- Connect to online social networks that want to hear about Brighton Fringe events
- Get your event in the third largest fringe festival in the world

What other costs are involved in running an event as part of Brighton Fringe?

Costs vary depending on the size and budget of your event; Brighton Fringe does not invite artists to perform, nor does it produce or pay anyone to be a part of the festival. Your event must be funded by you and your budget will need to include the following:

- Your production costs
- Venue hire
- Accommodation
- Wages and living costs
- Travel
- Marketing (adverts, posters etc.)
- Registration fee
- Licences
- Commission on ticket sales

For more information about funding, budgets and costs involved read the Guide to Funding your Brighton Fringe event.

How do I sell tickets for my event?

We run a box office so you don't have to, but you may want tickets available at another source; ie: the venue, so we make sure this is possible as well. You set the ticket prices and put forward any concessions or ticket offers. We ask that you allocate at least 30% of your tickets to the Brighton Fringe box office so that we can sell them through the website, in person and over the phone.

What commission do I pay on tickets?

We take 8.5% of the value of tickets sold through the Brighton Fringe Box Office; the rest is paid back to you within 6 weeks of the festival ending.

What is the average ticket price?

The average ticket price in 2012 was £8.70.

What additional advertising does Brighton Fringe offer?

There's plenty of opportunity to take out further advertising and if you have a registered event in Brighton Fringe you get a discount. Options include:

• Adverts in the Brighton Fringe brochure

• Adverts on the Brighton Fringe website

• Flyer inserts in mailed out in the Brighton Fringe brochures

• Advertising promotions, brochure and web advert deal

A rate card will be available to download from October 2012. Anyone registering an event in Brighton Fringe is entitled to a discount on the commercial advertising rates.

Whom do I contact for additional help and support?

For further help and information please contact us:
Brighton Fringe
5 Palace Place
BN1 1EF
Monday – Friday, 10am – 5pm
T: 01273 764900
E: participantservices@brightonfringe.org

"There's plenty of opportunity to take out further advertising and if you have a registered event in Brighton Fringe you get a discount"

Where can I get more information?

More information on the following will be available from our website as of the 23 October 2012. Go to **www.brightonfringe.org** for information about:

• How to Register

• How to run a Brighton Fringe venue

• Overseas artists and promoters & FEU information

• Registering a venue

• Finding a venue – searchable online venue directory

• Detailed list of registration prices & Bursary information

• Detailed list of additional advertising prices

- Fringe City (performing and flyering)
- Brighton flyer ban and obtaining a licence
- PRS

This article has been reproduced in its entirety with kind permission from Brighton Fringe. Brighton Fringe is the largest arts festival in England – you can find out more at **www.brightonfringe.org**.

A-Z of Arts Festivals in the UK

This is by no means a fully comprehensive list of the many arts festivals that take place throughout the year in the UK, but it's a good introduction to the wealth of different events that take place each year. Why not check out local listings to see what's happening near to you? It's always worth contacting festivals around six months before they take place if you want to take part. Please note that the dates given are only the 2012 festival dates, and so may vary from year to year.

ABERDEEN INTERNATIONAL YOUTH FESTIVAL

WWW.AIYF.ORG
INFO@AIYF.ORG
01224 213 800
MONTH: AUGUST

AIYF began its life as a classical music festival in the 1960s in Switzerland and moved to Aberdeen in 1973, where orchestras and chamber musicians from across Europe gathered to perform and collaborate in a festival environment. Forty years later and the festival has now grown, modernised and includes even more genres of the youth arts movement including dance, theatre, opera and world music. Over the years AIYF has hosted more than 25,000 young people from around the globe, making it one of the biggest and most successful gatherings of youth talent held anywhere in the world. AIYF brings more than 10 days of top class performances from around Scotland and the rest of the world.

ABSOLUT FRINGE

WWW.FRINGEFEST.COM
INFO@FRINGEFEST.COM
MONTH: SEPTEMBER

ABSOLUT Fringe is Ireland's largest multi-disciplinary arts festival. Now in its 18th year, the festival stages up to 525 events in over 40 venues, and around 150,000 people have at least one Fringe experience during the Festival. For 16 days the festival transforms Dublin into a 'dream factory', an exposé of great creative talent from around the globe. It is a platform for the best new, emerging Irish arts companies and a showcase for the best contemporary theatre and dance shows touring internationally. For artists, the Fringe facilitates an opportunity to innovate, to cross disciplines and boundaries and to find new ways and places to create work. ABSOLUT Fringe, unlike many Fringes internationally, is a wholly curated festival seeking innovative and daring work that impacts, moves and invigorates its audience.

ARTSFEST BIRMINGHAM

WWW.ARTSFEST.ORG.UK
ARTSFEST@BIRMINGHAM.GOV.UK
0121 464 5678
MONTH: SEPTEMBER

ArtsFest is one of the biggest, most popular urban festivals within the UK. It is also the UK's biggest FREE arts festival, which means there are no extortionate ticket prices for any of the 600 events that make up the festival each year, because there are no ticket prices at all! This means that you can see ballet to Bhangra, dub poetry to indie rock, without having to spend any money or queue for hours for tickets! What's more, as an urban festival – it comes without the mud! ArtsFest celebrates the West Midland region's astounding wealth of creative talent and shows the West Midland's region as the bustling cultural centre it is. It features performances, workshops, exhibitions, installations, talks and screenings, across the performing, visual and digital arts genres. It provides artists with the chance to showcase and celebrate their work and to raise their profile with the large numbers of visitors the festival attracts. Visitors get to sample everything from traditional to cutting edge arts and entertainment, all free of charge. ArtsFest is a festival for the young and old alike and we really do stick by our motto that there is something at ArtsFest for everybody to enjoy!

ARUNDEL FESTIVAL FRINGE

WWW.ARUNDELFESTIVAL.CO.UK
MONTH: AUGUST-SEPTEMBER
Established fringe festival run alongside official Arundel Festival.

ASHBOURNE FESTIVAL

WWW.ASHBOURNEFESTIVAL.ORG
INFO@ASHBOURNEFESTIVAL.ORG
MONTH: JUNE – JULY

Ashbourne Arts and Ashbourne Festival celebrated their tenth anniversary in 2009. The company was granted Charitable status in July 2007 and its primary focus is to organise a two-week long Festival during June and July each year. The Festival continues to grow in stature, now attracting support from major funders and internationally known performers to this charming rural area. But not forgetting its community origins, it continues to provide for the cultural needs of the town and surrounding area.

BATH FRINGE FESTIVAL

WWW.BATHFRINGE.CO.UK
ADMIN@BATHFRINGE.CO.UK
MONTH: MAY-JUNE

Bath Fringe is a 17-Day festival of all the artforms we can find (and some that don't have names yet) in the Beautiful City of Bath, and with the collaboration of many of its Beautiful & Talented population. 170-odd events (some odder than others), performers from around the world and from next door, in places from the Spiegeltent, to the secret rooms of

Bath, to the streets and cafés, to cyberspace and between your ears, and of course in all the city's best venues...

BEDFRINGE
THE PLACE THEATRE
BRADGATE ROAD
BEDFORD
MK40 3DE
012 3426 9519
WWW.BEDFRINGE.CO.UK
ADMIN@BEDFRINGE.COM
MONTH: JULY
Since 2007 Bedfringe has seen over 300 acts pass through its doors making it one of the fastest growing performing arts festivals in the UK. In 2011 Over 165 people performed in 50 events in 10 venues over 2 weeks. Over the years Bedfringe has occupied many local venues turning them into fully functional performance spaces. These venues include The Swan Hotel, The Civic Theatre, The Harpur Suite, The Howard Room and Bedford Gallery. As well as other more established spaces including The Bedford Corn Exchange, The Place Theatre, Bedford Theatre, South Bank Arts Centre, Esquires and The Ent Shed.

BELFAST FESTIVAL
WWW.BELFASTFESTIVAL.COM
MONTH: OCTOBER – NOVEMBER
Ireland's largest international arts festival, with a plethora of theatre and comedy acts. One of the Festival's key roles is as an advocate of local work,

giving Belfast's arts practitioners a unique opportunity to present their work on an international platform.

BEWDLEY FESTIVAL
WWW.BEWDLEYFESTIVAL.ORG.UK
ADMIN@BEWDLEYFESTIVAL.ORG.UK
MONTH: OCTOBER
Festival featuring drama, comedy, music and visual arts, with a range of fringe events.

BRIGHTON FESTIVAL FRINGE
01273 764 900
WWW.BRIGHTONFESTIVALFRINGE.ORG.UK
PARTICIPANTSERVICES@BRIGHTONFRINGE.ORG
MONTH: MAY
Brighton Fringe is the largest arts festival in England and what makes it exceptional is that it is set in a city with a unique heritage that has set the pace, diversity, creativity and innovative thinking in the city and beyond. It sets out to stimulate, educate and entertain a wide audience by providing a showcase for diverse art forms. It is also a completely open access festival, which means anyone can put on an event and be included in the brochure and website listings on payment of a fee. By definition, Brighton Fringe can include any art form.No artistic judgment or selection criteria are imposed on partici-pants, enabling the development of both new and established work to attract fresh audiences, press and promoters.

BROUHAHA INTERNATIONAL STREET FESTIVAL (MERSEYSIDE)

WWW.BROUHAHA.UK.COM

INFO@BROUHAHA.UK.COM

MONTH: AUGUST

Brouhaha International is a professional arts organisation that operates within local and international contexts. Our mission is 'To develop and deliver quality arts projects and programmes that meet the needs of children, young people and adults from a range of diverse communities and neighbourhoods at a local, national and international level'.

BURY ST EDMUNDS FRINGE FESTIVAL

WWW.BURYFRINGE.COM

CLAIRE@BURYFRINGE.COM

MONTH: APRIL

With an extensive and varied programme spanning a fortnight of events and shows, hosted by numerous venues throughout the town of Bury St Edmunds, there will be something to involve and appeal to every single member of our community. We are an open-access festival and as such are keen to involve as many people and local groups as possible. Whatever your talent, we will aim to find a place for you during the Fringe! We're all about the feel-good factor and intend to place a smile firmly on the faces of all those who live, work, study and socialise in our town.

BUXTON FESTIVAL FRINGE

32 GREEN LANE

BUXTON SK17 9DL

WWW.BUXTONFRINGE.ORG.UK

MONTH: JULY

Buxton Festival Fringe began in 1980 to run concurrently with the world-renowned Buxton Festival, with international opera and high profile literary talks at its core. The Fringe goes from strength to strength each year and now has a respected and professional image with a full colour brochure, reviews of all shows, prize funds and many artists using it as a preview before appearing at Edinburgh Festival Fringe. The Fringe provides a showcase for performers and artists of all kinds in a variety of venues. Dance, drama, music, poetry, comedy, film, exhibitions and magic are just some of the forms that have appeared – we welcome all genres. The Fringe Committee does not undertake any selection, censorship, financing or selective promotion of individual events.

CAMBRIDGE FRINGE FESTIVAL

WWW.CAMFRINGE.COM

INFO@CAMFRINGE.COM

MONTH: JULY-AUGUST

Cambridge Fringe Festival carries on that great tradition of freedom of expression for the arts, by creating a fringe festival that supports an open arts policy with no artistic vetting. For us as organisers it is about bringing you extraordinary performances and emerging talents, often as part of non-commercial shows. It's about that now little used showbiz word "Variety".

CAMDEN FRINGE

THE ETCETERA THEATRE
265 CAMDEN HIGH STREET
LONDON NW1 7BU
WWW.CAMDENFRINGE.COM
ADMIN@CAMDENFRINGE.ORG
MONTH: JULY AND AUGUST

The Camden Fringe was set-up by Zena Barrie and Michelle Flower for It's Alright For Some Ltd, who produced comedy at the Edinburgh Fringe Festival from 2002 – 2006 and started running the Etcetera Theatre in Camden since the beginning of 2004. The first Camden Fringe took place in August 2006 at the Etcetera Theatre and included 57 performances by 22 acts over a 4 week period. It has grown steadily since then. The 2010 Camden Fringe was made of 652 performances in 8 venues. The Camden Fringe aims to give anyone the chance to perform and showcase their talents, from very experienced performers and companies to ambitious newcomers.

CANTERBURY FESTIVAL

WWW.CANTERBURYFESTIVAL.CO.UK
INFO@CANTERBURYFESTIVAL.CO.UK
MONTH: OCTOBER

The Canterbury Festival is Kent's International Arts Festival, the largest festival of arts and culture in the region, and one of the most important cultural events in the South East. The Festival attracts an audience of nearly 80,000 people of all ages to free and ticketed events, drawn from across Kent, London and the South East. With over two hundred events in two weeks there is something to suit everyone from classical music to contemporary dance, and from comedy to world music with theatre, walks, talks, visual arts, and much more.

CHELSEA FESTIVAL

WWW.CHELSEAARTSFESTIVAL.ORG
INFO@CHELSEAARTSFESTIVAL.ORG
MONTH: JULY

The chelsea:artsfestival exists to celebrate this unique area and its vital contribution to London's diverse culture; to present the highest quality and distinctive performance; and to ensure that future generations are ever more switched on to all things cultural.

DUBLIN THEATRE FESTIVAL

WWW.DUBLINTHEATREFESTIVAL.COM
INFO@DUBLINTHEATREFESTIVAL.COM
MONTH: SEPTEMBER – OCTOBER

Our policy is to bring the best available international theatre to Dublin and to balance the programme with Irish productions, especially new plays. The Festival is regarded as the oldest established specialist theatre festival in Europe. Unlike Edinburgh, opera, music and dance do not form a major element of the programme.

THE DYLAN THOMAS FRINGE FESTIVAL

WWW.DYLANTHOMASFRINGE.COM
INFO@DYLANTHOMASFRINGE.COM
MONTH: SEPTEMBER – OCTOBER

The Dylan Thomas Fringe exists to provide a showcase for the best in up and coming talent in the performing arts from Swansea and South West Wales, combined with a range of acts from further afield. Established in 2005, following a successful pilot event the previous year, the Fringe has grown steadily incorporating a wide array of performers and events. Past Fringes have featured Rob Brydon, Harry Hill, Ardal O'Hanlon, Jimmy Carr, James Taylor Quartet, and David McAlmont; alongside a host of eclectic local and national performers.

EDINBURGH FESTIVAL FRINGE

180 HIGH STREET
EDINBURGH EH1 1QS
UNITED KINGDOM
0131 226 0026
WWW.EDFRINGE.COM
ADMIN@EDFRINGE.COM
MONTH: AUGUST

The Edinburgh Festival Fringe is the largest arts festival in the world and takes place every August for three weeks in Scotland's capital city. Every year thousands of performers take to a multitude of stages all over Edinburgh to present shows for every taste. From big names in the world of entertainment to unknown artists looking to build their careers, the festival caters for everyone and includes theatre, comedy, dance, physical theatre, musicals, operas, music, exhibitions and events.

GRASSINGTON FESTIVAL OF MUSIC AND ARTS

WWW.GRASSINGTON-FESTIVAL.ORG.UK
ARTS@GRASSINGTON-FESTIVAL.ORG.UK
MONTH: JUNE

For the last two weeks of June each year, Grassington comes alive in a myriad of colours and creativity as artists, bands, art enthusiasts and local people collaborate to entertain and inspire with unusual and unique live performances, from music, dance and street theatre to workshops, talks, walks and creative challenges. The now nationally renowned festival provides an affordable opportunity for everyone to appreciate the arts in all forms, from classical to comedy. Held in and around this beautiful Yorkshire Dales village, Grassington Festival also runs a variety of workshops and walks, encouraging people to learn and improve their own skills, and appreciate the stunning surrounding countryside, in addition to enjoying world class entertainment.

HEBDEN BRIDGE ART FESTIVAL

HBAF.CO.UK

MONTH: JUNE-JULY

An annual highlight for the Calder Valley, Hebden bridge Arts Festival brings the best national and international artists and performers to the area each summer for a celebration of comedy, music, dance, drama, literature, and visual arts.

LONDON INTERNATIONAL FESTIVAL OF THEATRE (LIFT)

WWW.LIFTFESTIVAL.COM

INFO@LIFTFESTIVAL.COM

Established in 1981 by Rose Fenton and Lucy Neal, LIFT, London International Festival of Theatre, has risen to become one of the most important events in the British arts scene, with an influence that reaches far beyond London. Working with artists from across the world to find new ways of seeing the city, LIFT's rich and varied programming has presented extraordinary events in both conventional theatres and in more unusual spaces such as disused power stations, churches and canal basins. Founded on the conviction that theatre has the power to surprise and stimulate as well as entertain, LIFT has constantly challenged the status quo and continues to actively engage different audiences and communities. LIFT both leads and looks over the ever-changing landscape of contemporary theatre and London itself, offering a panoramic view that will take your breath away.

LLANGOLLEN FRINGE FESTIVAL

WWW.LLANGOLLENFRINGE.CO.UK

INFO@LLANGOLLENFRINGE.CO.UK

MONTH: JULY

From its first year in an impromptu tent on an out-of-town playing field through to its present fixed canolfan Town Hall location, via a converted weavers' shed, the Fringe has increased its reputation with every year. Initially the Fringe's mission statement was "to provide entertainment and education to the community of Llangollen, North Wales". This mission has grown with the festival, and now, in addition to offering inspiring, eclectic and high profile events, we actively promote the concept of sustainability – culturally, socially, economically and environmentally.

MANCHESTER INTERNATIONAL FESTIVAL

WWW.MIF.CO.UK

INFO@MIF.CO.UK

MONTH: JUNE – JULY

Manchester International Festival is the world's first festival of original, new work and special events, and takes place biennially in Manchester, UK. The Festival launched in 2007 as an artist-led, commissioning festival presenting new works from across the spectrum of performing arts, visual arts and popular culture.

OXFRINGE

WWW.OXFRINGE.COM

MONTH: MAY – JUNE

Oxfringe is not for profit and is run for the prime purpose of promoting upcoming artists who are not yet established and to provide arts entertainment for the benefit of the community of Oxford and for audiences from further afield. Its mission is to provide an open access multi-genre fringe festival for Oxford, including comedy, drama, music of all kinds, literary fringe and mixed genre events, to support new and emerging talent across the arts. Oxfringe organises a small number of headline shows, performer preview opportunities and free community events.

PULSE FRINGE FESTIVAL (IPSWICH)

WWW.PULSEFRINGE.COM

MONTH: MAY – JUNE

Showcasing comedy and drama in the East of England.

SALISBURY INTERNATIONAL ARTS FESTIVAL

WWW.SALISBURYFESTIVAL.CO.UK

INFO@SALISBURYFESTIVAL.CO.UK

MONTH: MAY – JUNE

The Festival blazed into life in July 1973. Since then, over a million people have enjoyed outstanding performances of theatre, dance, film and every kind of music, plus literary events and the visual arts. From mid-May to early June each year, the beautiful historic city of Salisbury is transformed as people flock to the Festival, enjoying both ticketed events and free performances.

SEDBERGH FESTIVAL OF BOOKS AND DRAMA

WWW.SEDBERGH.ORG.UK/BOOKFESTIVAL

STRATFORD UPON AVON FRINGE

10-11 SHEEP STREET

STRATFORD-UPON-AVON

WARWICKSHIRE CV37 6EF

01789 299011

WWW.STRATFORDFRINGE.CO.UK

INFO@STRATFORDFRINGE.CO.UK

MONTH: JUNE

Fringe comedy, dance, theatre, poetry, and music in Stratford-upon-Avon.

WEXFORD FRINGE FESTIVAL

WWW.WEXFORDFRINGE.IE

MONTH: OCTOBER – NOVEMBER

Art exhibitions, recitals, dance, music, and specially themed children's events.

The Big 15: The Top Employers on Stage Jobs Pro

To give you an idea of the big players in the theatre industry here are the Top 15 Employers on Stage Jobs Pro. We've also included the number of Stage Jobs Pro Members who have worked for each company. These figures are correct at the time of going to print.

AMBASSADOR THEATRE GROUP
ATG TICKETS CUSTOMER CONTACT CENTRE
4TH FLOOR
PRINCE CONSORT HOUSE
LONDON
SE1 7TJ
WWW.ATGTICKETS.COM
SJP MEMBERS: **1,042**

Co-founded by Howard Panter and Rosemary Squire in 1992, the Ambassador Theatre Group Ltd (ATG) is the largest owner/operator of theatres in the UK with 39 venues, an internationally recognised theatre producer and a leader in theatre ticketing services through ATG Tickets. ATG has been behind some of the most successful and innovative productions in Britain and internationally. Current and recent ATG co-productions include the Lincoln Center's production of Rodgers & Hammerstein's South Pacific (London and UK Tour); All New People starring Zach Braff (Manchester and London); Ghost the Musical (Manchester, London and Broadway); Posh/Jumpy (a Royal Court Season at the Duke of York's); Dolly Parton's 9 to 5 The Musical (Manchester, UK Tour and London); Dandy Dick starring Patricia Hodge and Nicholas Le Prevost (Brighton, UK Tour and London); Matthew Bourne's The Nutcracker! (Sadler's Wells and UK Tour); Legally Blonde the Musical (London and UK Tour); Monty Python's Spamalot by Eric Idle (London and UK Tour); Being Shakespeare starring Simon Callow (London, UK Tour and New York); The Misanthrope starring Damian Lewis and Keira Knightley (London); the critically acclaimed award-winning musical West Side Story (Sadler's Wells and UK Tour); Elling starring John Simm (London); Guys and Dolls starring Ewan McGregor (London) and The Rocky Horror Show (London and UK Tour).

BILL KENWRIGHT LTD
BKL HOUSE
1 VENICE WALK
LONDON W2 1RR
UNITED KINGDOM
WWW.KENWRIGHT.COM
INFO@KENWRIGHT.COM
SJP MEMBERS: **829**

Bill Kenwright Ltd is the UK's largest independent theatre and film production company. Recent West End productions include: The Wizard of Oz (Palladium); The Country Girl (Apollo); Bedroom Farce (Duke of York's); A Daughter's a Daughter (Trafalgar Studios); Dreamboats and Petticoats (Playhouse); On the Waterfront (Haymarket); Woman In Mind (Haymarket); Plague Over England (Duchess); Sunset Boulevard (Comedy); The Vortex (Apollo); Absurd Person Singular (Garrick); Joseph and the Amazing Technicolor Dreamcoat (Adelphi); The Letter (Wyndham's); Treats (Garrick); The Glass Menagerie (Apollo); Cabaret (Lyric), The Canterbury Tales (RSC – Gielgud); The Crucible (RSC – Gielgud); Whistle Down the Wind (Palace); A Man for All Seasons (Theatre Royal, Haymarket); The Night of the Iguana (Lyric); Scrooge (London Palladium); A Few Good Men (Haymarket); The Big Life (Apollo); Elmina's Kitchen (Garrick); Festen (Lyric); Judi Dench in All's Well That Ends Well (RSC – Gielgud); Hay Fever (Haymarket); Filumena (Piccadilly) and The Gift of the Gorgon (Wyndham's); The Taming of the Shrew and The Tamer Tamed (RSC – Queen's); The Secret Rapture (Lyric); the RSC Jacobean season (Gielgud); Via Dolorosa (Duchess); Sleuth (Apollo); The Constant Wife (Lyric); Cat on a Hot Tin Roof (Lyric); Ghosts (Comedy); Fallen Angels (Apollo); Long Day's Journey Into Night (Lyric); Brief Encounter (Lyric); Miss Julie (Haymarket); Stepping Out (Albery); Hurlyburly (Queen's); Lady Windermere's Fan (Haymarket); Passion (Queen's); Company (Albery); The Miracle Worker (Wyndham's); No Man's Land and Moonlight (Comedy). Directed by Peter Hall: Mind Millie for Me, The Master Builder and Jessica Lange in A Streetcar Named Desire (Haymarket); The School for Wives (Piccadilly); Hamlet and An Absolute Turkey (Gielgud); Lysistrata (Old Vic, Athens); Separate Tables (Albery); She Stoops to Conquer (Queen's); Waiting for Godot, The Misanthrope, Major Barbara, and Kafka's Dick (Piccadilly).

ROYAL SHAKESPEARE COMPANY

ROYAL SHAKESPEARE THEATRE
WATERSIDE
STRATFORD-UPON-AVON
WARWICKSHIRE
CV37 6BB
WWW.RSC.ORG.UK
JOBS@RSC.ORG.UK
SJP MEMBERS: **818**

The RSC is one of the world's best known theatre companies. Our job is to connect and help others connect with Shakespeare and produce bold, ambitious work with living writers, actors and artists. We are an ensemble company so everyone here, from directors, writers and actors to production, technical and administrative staff, has a part to play in creating distinctive theatre. We believe in taking risks and pushing creative boundaries – finding new ways of doing things and learning through action. Our audiences are at the heart of all we do and we want to challenge, inspire and involve them. Our home is in Stratford-upon-Avon and in 2010 we reopened the Royal Shakespeare and Swan theatres after a £112.8m transformation to bring actors and audiences closer together. We play regularly in London, Newcastle upon Tyne and on tour across the UK and the world. As well as the plays of Shakespeare and his contemporaries, we produce new work from living artists and develop creative links with theatre-makers from around the world.

QDOS ENTERTAINMENT

QDOS HOUSE
QUEEN MARGARETS ROAD
SCARBOROUGH
NORTH YORKSHIRE
YO11 2YH
WWW.QDOSENTERTAINMENT.COM
INFO@QDOSENTERTAINMENT.CO.UK
SJP MEMBERS: **735**

Chaired by Nick Thomas, the company he created in 1986 is now one of the largest, broad-based entertainment Groups in the UK. Focussed on family entertainment and traditional values, the Group has grown both organically and through a steady 'buy & build' strategy focusing on businesses that complement the original model, managed by a coherent holding company.

NATIONAL THEATRE

SOUTH BANK
LONDON SE1 9PX
WWW.NATIONALTHEATRE.ORG.UK
INFO@NATIONALTHEATRE.ORG.UK
SJP MEMBERS: **716**

The National Theatre stages over 20 theatre productions a year. These are put on in our three auditoriums – the Olivier, Lyttelton and Cottesloe Theatres – and in these three theatres, we present a mix of new plays and classics, with up to six productions in repertory at any one time.

UK Productions
Churchmill House,
Ockford Road,
Godalming,
Surrey.
GU7 1QY
WWW.UKPRODUCTIONS.CO.UK
MAIL@UKPRODUCTIONS.CO.UK
SJP MEMBERS: **625**

UK Productions was formed in 1995 to produce musicals and pantomimes, for which they are now one of the country's most prolific producers .West End producing credits include Seven Brides for Seven Brothers (Theatre Royal, Haymarket). Other producing credits for national and international tours of musicals include Oklahoma! (2010) Singin' in the Rain (2009), Disney's Beauty & the Beast (2005 – 2010), South Pacific (2007/8), Seven Brides for Seven Brothers (2001/2, 2005/6, 2008/9), Jekyll and Hyde – The Musical (2004/5), Carousel (2003/4 and 2000), Fiddler on the Roof (2008, 2003), Anything Goes (2001), The Pirates of Penzance (1998/9), 42nd Street (1997, 1999, 2000, 2007), and Barnum (1995/6). UK Productions have a passion for pantomime, and produce shows for a number of theatres nationwide. They apply the same high standards to these productions as they do to their touring musicals. Whether large or small they all receive the UK Productions treatment of all-star casts in traditional shows backed by lavish sets and costumes. UK Productions have produced a number of outdoor events and are responsible for the creation and production of The Stansted Park Proms, an annual two-day open-air concert playing to up to 10,000 people a night in the grounds of Stansted House, a stately home in the heart of Hampshire. The concerts feature live orchestras and bands and each evening culminates in our now legendary fantastic fireworks finales.

Cameron Mackintosh Limited
1 Bedford Square
London
WC1B 3RB
INFO@CAMACK.CO.UK
WWW.CAMERONMACKINTOSH.COM
SJP MEMBERS: **576**

Cameron Mackintosh has produced numerous highly successful musicals, including My Fair Lady, Oklahoma!, a revival of Oliver!, Side by Side by Sondheim, Cats, Song and Dance, Little Shop of Horrors, Blondel, Abbacadabra, Les Miserables, The Phantom of the Opera, Follies, Mary Poppins, Avenue Q, Hair. Cameron Mackintosh owns seven theatres in London's West End, the Queen's, Gielgud, Prince of Wales, Novello, Prince Edward, Noël Coward and Wyndham's, all of which have undergone spectacular refurbishment.

ROYAL OPERA HOUSE
COVENT GARDEN
LONDON WC2E 9DD
WWW.ROH.ORG.UK
SJP MEMBERS: **540**

The Royal Opera, under the direction of Antonio Pappano, is one of the world's leading opera companies. Based in the iconic Covent Garden theatre, it is renowned for its outstanding perform-ances of both traditional opera as well as commissioning new works by today's leading opera composers such as Harrison Birtwistle, Mark-Anthony Turnage and Thomas Ades.

ENGLISH NATIONAL OPERA (ENO)
LONDON COLISEUM
ST. MARTIN'S LANE
LONDON WC2N 4ES
WWW.ENO.ORG
FEEDBACK@ENO.ORG
SJP MEMBERS: **537**

ENO is creating the future of opera: presenting award winning work that is new, exciting and surprising. Collaborating with creative talent from across the arts we stage more new productions and contemporary opera than any other UK opera company. We have a world class reputation for distinctive and highly theatrical productions which has resulted in many high profile artistic partnerships with opera houses and festivals around the world, including the Metropolitan Opera, New York and Bayerische Staatsoper,

Munich. We are committed to creating new audiences for opera through English language performances which are affordable and accessible to everyone. We provide unique opportunities and pathways for British singers, conductors, directors and designers.

CHICHESTER FESTIVAL THEATRE
OAKLANDS PARK
CHICHESTER
WEST SUSSEX
PO19 6AP
WWW.CFT.ORG.UK
SJP MEMBERS: **520**

It was Sir Laurence Olivier's vision that the theatre would produce several shows to run in repertoire sharing the same ensemble cast. And so it was that the theatre opened in 1962 with a 'festival' of three shows which were to run for three weeks – hence Festival Theatre and Festival Season. 2012 will mark the 50th Anniversary of the opening of the Theatre and celebrations commence with the transfer of two sell-out productions from the 2011 Festival Season: Singin' in the Rain, directed by Jonathan Church, to the Palace Theatre from February and Sweeney Todd, featuring Michael Ball and Imelda Staunton, into the Adelphi Theatre from March. Patrick Stewart will also reprise his lead role in Bingo by Edward Bond, directed by Chichester Festival Theatre Associate Director Angus Jackson, in a co-production at the Young Vic opening in the New Year.

BRISTOL OLD VIC
THEATRE ROYAL
KING STREET
BRISTOL BS1 4ED
WWW.BRISTOLOLDVIC.ORG.UK
STAGEDOOR@BRISTOLOLDVIC.ORG.UK
SJP MEMBERS: **498**

BIRMINGHAM REPERTORY THEATRE
ST GEORGE'S COURT
ALBION STREET,
BIRMINGHAM
B1 3AH
WWW.BIRMINGHAM-REP.CO.UK
STAGE.DOOR@BIRMINGHAM-REP.CO.UK
SJP MEMBERS: 373
The REP's mission has always been to produce excellent theatrical experiences, to entertain, enlighten and engage audiences and, wherever possible, to reflect the diversity of Birmingham and the surrounding region. This supports our vision, which is to 'Inspire the city of Birmingham to a lifelong love of theatre'. Making theatre from scratch remains at the heart of the theatre's work. Birmingham and the Black Country have historically been known as the workshop of the world. They are now celebrated as great cultural workshops too. Birmingham City Council vision has put cultural ingenuity at the centre of regeneration and The REP is a force at the heart of that vision.

WEST YORKSHIRE PLAYHOUSE
PLAYHOUSE SQUARE
QUARRY HILL
LEEDS
LS2 7UP
WWW.WYP.ORG.UK
INFO@WYP.ORG.UK
SJP MEMBERS: **368**
Since opening in 1990, West Yorkshire Playhouse has established a national and international reputation. We provide both a thriving focal point for the communities of West Yorkshire and theatre of the highest standard for audiences throughout the region and beyond. The Playhouse has two theatres, the Quarry with 750 seats and the smaller, more flexible Courtyard with 350 seats. Alongside its work on stage, the Playhouse continues to lead the theatre industry in the ambition and scope of its education and community work. The Playhouse is a producing theatre, building and rehearsing our own shows in our home in the city of Leeds. We regularly collaborate with other major regional producing theatres and companies and a full list of shows from 1990 can be found in our online archive. We tour our shows nationally and have seen many shows transfer to the West End. Our most recent West End Transfer was Othello (2009) to Trafalgar Studios featuring Lenny Henry, a co-production with Northern Broadsides. West Yorkshire Playhouse is a significant employer in the region, with over 200 staff. Jobs vary

from technicians, carpenters and metal-workers, lighting and sound designers and operators, wardrobe and wigs, to front of house customer service and communication, production administration and arts development.

SCOTTISH OPERA

39 ELMBANK CRESCENT
GLASGOW G2 4PT
WWW.SCOTTISHOPERA.ORG.UK
INFORMATION@SCOTTISHOPERA.ORG.UK
SJP MEMBERS: **345**

Scottish Opera is Scotland's national opera company and the largest performing arts organisation in Scotland. It was founded by Alexander Gibson and was inaugurated with a production of Madama Butterfly at the King's Theatre in Glasgow. In 1974 Scottish Opera purchased the Theatre Royal Glasgow, which reopened in 1975 as Scotland's first national opera house. The Orchestra of Scottish Opera was founded in 1980.

ROYAL COURT THEATRE

SLOANE SQUARE
LONDON SW1W 8AS
WWW.ROYALCOURTTHEATRE.COM
INFO@ROYALCOURTTHEATRE.COM
SJP MEMBERS: **329**

The Royal Court Theatre is Britain's leading national company dedicated to new work by innovative writers from the UK and around the world. The theatre's pivotal role in promoting new voices is undisputed – the New York Times described it as 'the most important theatre in Europe'. The Royal Court receives and considers an extraordinary quantity of new work and, each year, presents an ambitious programme in its two venues at Sloane Square in London. In recent years, the Royal Court has also staged productions in New York, Sydney, Brussels, Toronto and Dublin. In addition to its high profile productions, the Royal Court facilitates international work at a grass roots level, developing exchanges which bring young writers to Britain and sending British writers, actors and directors to work with artists around the world. The Royal Court Young Writers Programme also works to develop new voices with a biennial Festival and year-round development work for writers under 26. The Royal Court's success has inspired confidence in theatres across the world and, whereas new plays were once viewed as a risk, they are now at the heart of a revival of interest among artists and audiences alike.

International & Cruise Ship Work

One of the most exciting things about a career in theatre is the opportunity it affords to work abroad, most commonly as part of an internationally touring theatre company or on board a cruise ship. We asked three Stage Jobs Pro members about their experiences doing just that: what they did, what they learned and how it lead to where they are now.

Andrew G. Smith – 'A Touring Life'

Hello to all of you out there, curious about working abroad. I've always loved to travel, and am delighted by the opportunities that being in this business gives me. During my heavy touring years I met many travelers, from divers in Thailand to Dutch clothing quality controllers flying to factories in China, from project managers in Hong Kong to adventure bikers in Western Canada. One of the strangest persons I met when traveling was a German tattooist living on Ko Pha Ngan, who spent way more time relaxing in the sun than actually tattooing.

The world is a big, interesting and breathtaking place, and in my opinion travelling being part of work is the most enjoyable and exciting thing one could ever do.

I first toured in 1994. At first, I was unsure if I wanted to tour – I'd been in the theatre business for a couple of years, had a good reputation and was getting steady work. I liked my neighborhood and the apartment I'd lucked into finding, and I was happily dating.

A colleague I'd met that summer at the Banff Centre was hired as the Technical Director for the local ballet company, and was recruiting touring staff. He liked my enthusiasm and work, and invited me aboard as one of the department heads. It took him three tries before I accepted. I worried I'd lose what I'd built up – I was being hired semi-permanently on show runs and show builds in local theatres, and I didn't want to lose this status as a reliable technician.

As it turned out, I enjoyed the tours so much that I based all other work around them for three full years. Touring with a ballet company was so much fun. It left two strong impressions: you're part of a team, bringing your show into different auditoriums, solving problems on the fly. The local crew can be a great help with problem solving; it really does pay to seek their advice.

Then at the end of the workday, you're exploring a new city; perhaps one you'd never go to otherwise. And the best thing is: you're paid to do it.

After those three years, I was offered a terrific full time job mentoring and had to give up the ballet tours. Yet after two years of the mentoring job I was yearning to travel again. Shortly after, I received a call to tour from a colleague who worked for a circus company (yes – that company!), suggesting I apply for a job. Initially I was again torn between giving up what I'd worked hard to build up and traveling, but travel won out. That tour became a decade on the road and took me to Japan, Europe, the US, eastern Canada and China, and I worked on five consecutive shows.

Many people who are offered a touring job decide to give it a year – pack up your life into storage boxes, vacate your apartment or find renters for your house. Either sell your car or store it. Make plans for your partner to either join you or to see each other. Skype really helps, but nothing beats seeing the person in the flesh.

Maybe touring isn't for you and you can simply return home. Or maybe it's a life changing experience, and you'll never be able to return to your old life.

A typical profile of a touring person is to be friendly, calm, proactive, and great in a team environment. Take care of your co-workers, local staff, performers and you'll do well.

A piece of advice, shared with me when I first joined the circus: have a hobby or interests. Without this, it's easy to spend your whole time partying and end up feeling like you've missed out. The hobby can be anything – photography, creating music, knitting, writing a blog. It can even be travel itself – exploring the city or country where you're working.

> **"A typical profile of a touring person is to be friendly, calm, proactive, and great in a team environment"**

Typically a touring show will take care of you, it's in their interest to make sure you get from point A to B, that you have accommodation and food to eat. Different companies offer different levels of care and different levels of remuneration.

So – what do you take with you on tour?

Four-wheel rolling suitcases are my favorite as they're much easier to manage between travel points. Plus you can use them like dollies and load a backpack or hockey bag on top, so you don't have to carry them on your shoulder. They also work as a seat when all the others are taken.

A fairly compact computer loaded with your favorite music, programs, files (always keep your up to date CV on it), photos, and movies. Satellite speakers are a must (Bose Musicmonitor gets my vote). Consider a Kindle or tablet to read books and bring with you to the local coffee shop for wifi use.

In many countries you can get chips for your unlocked phone, and charge up as you go. I would bring enough pairs of socks, underwear and shirts to tide you over between days off and the search for a Laundromat. Yes, you can get the hotel where you're staying to do your laundry, but I always found it more enjoyable to google the closest Laundromat and explore the area around it.

Always keep a set of nice clothes with you for openings or special events, and of course clothes you can wear to go out in.

Maybe even consider room decoration, personal things that make your hotel room feel more welcoming. A bed throw, a colored scarf to cover the shade on your bedside lamp (careful here – don't let it touch the lightbulb!), colored string lights. I've tried a few different things – I toured with an ivy plant for a couple of months that eventually was blown off my balcony into a courtyard in a huge storm! Also, one of those fake sleeping cats which surprised housekeeping (eventually the cat was turned into a football when I left my room in the care of some friends for an hour). I suggest you check in with your colleagues and the performers; ask what they bring with them. Visit their rooms and see what they do to make touring enjoyable.

The hardest thing about touring... is not touring! Once you've lived a touring life, it's very hard to stop. Maybe all your friends are on the tour, and perhaps a settled life looked appealing from a distance. If you've toured for a while, make sure you've got plenty of challenges when you stop and that the trade off is worth it. Still, count on it taking half a year to a year to adjust!

Andrew G. Smith is Head of Stage Carpentry & Stage Carpentry Training at The Banff Centre. You can find him on LinkedIn: Andrew G. Smith.

Jenni Morris – 'Cruise Ships & China'

I graduated with a BA (Hons) in Performance Management from Bretton Hall College of the University of Leeds in 2001. I thought I wanted to go into Technical Stage Management at the time. After graduating I went travelling in Australia for a year with a working holiday visa. When I got back to the UK I needed to find a job but I had trouble getting into the theatre industry. I was applying for everything but as I was pretty fresh out of University it wasn't easy. I worked in a school as a Learning Support Assistant while I applied for every job in theatre I could find, including walking around the West End on a regular basis handing my CV in to the theatres. I was applying for everything from backstage tech to front of house. I did do some Front of House work and a couple of short term stage management contracts, but nothing permanent.

I'd been back in the country a year when I had a letter from Princess Cruises with an application form to fill in to be Stage Crew as I'd applied for a job advertised in The Stage. I didn't even remember applying as I was applying for so much. The same day I got a phone call to see if I could make an interview the following week as some spaces had become available. I went along to the interview and a week later I got a phone call telling me that I'd got the job, I would be joining the Coral Princess in Fort Lauderdale, Florida

to cruise the Caribbean, then through the Panama Canal and up to Alaska. As you can imagine I was extremely excited. A great job and being paid to see the world!

I stayed with Princess Cruises for four years. I was Stage Crew for the first year. This included: running backstage tracks for the big production shows; the set up, strikes and running of all the shows in all of the entertainment venues on board; running spot light for various shows and assisting with all theatre maintenance, including lighting and automation.

A typical day in the life of the Stage Crew on a sea day would be getting up to set up a working kitchen on stage for the cooking demonstration, eating some of the food cooked on stage, striking the set so the stage was ready for the Port and Shopping talk, then head to the other theatre to set up Bingo and stay there for the Bingo to play music when people win and make sure the microphones and the Bingo machine are working. Then we would strike Bingo and set up for line dancing, play the music and dance along with the Cruise Staff (or sit down and amuse yourself by watching the passengers trying to dance on a rocky ship). We would set up a band by the pool side and be present for any pool games to play music and look after the microphones. Perhaps we might run a movie in the theatre in the afternoon before setting the stage for the evening's big production show. Then we'd head to the Crew Mess or get dressed up and head out to eat in the Passenger buffet. Then back to the theatre for the evening's show, which would be a big production show, or comedians, singers, magicians, ventriloquists, hypnotists etc. Then after the show we would head to the crew bar for a drink, have a dance at the Crew Disco or head to someone's cabin for a cabin party. There is a lot of partying!

When the ship was in port one or two people would stay on the ship as duty to cover the small events to keep the few passengers who remain on board entertained. The rest of us would get off the ship and head to the beach, or a bar, or hire a boat or moped to tour around some Caribbean islands, or perhaps hike up a mountain in Alaska. Just make sure you get back to the ship on time before it sails away. The crew can sign up to go on passenger tours as they sometimes need extra chaperones.

The person in charge of the Stage Crew was the Crew Chief, who would do the scheduling for the whole production department: Production Manager; LX tech; Sound tech; and 10 stage crew, as well as being in charge of the Automation on board. On ships there is a lot of automation so that the shows can be big without using up too much space. In the main

theatre there were 2 large lifts, a performer lift, 9 serepid tracks, 26 line sets, several moving LX bars and a rain curtain. I started training with the Crew Chief on my time off. In the second theatre there were 3 revolving stages with 13 lifts. I was soon running some of the production shows and I got promoted to Crew Chief. This was a great experience, programming automation for some new shows coming in and running the big production shows, as well as doing the schedule each night ready for the next day to ensure all the events were covered by our department.

Each contract was between three and six months and I got to see a lot of amazing places over the four years I was with Princess. I went to the Caribbean several times, the Panama Canal, Mexican Riviera, Alaska, Canada and Asia. The

"Each contract was between three and six months and I got to see a lot of amazing places over the four years"

company paid for flights to the ship and back to your home airport. They pay for your insurance and we got paid in US dollars, in cash each month. You don't have to pay for food or accommodation. The only things you pay for is anything you buy when you're off the ship - normally food, drink and souvenirs. When you pick up your pay from the crew office you then move to the next window to give some money back to pay your bar bill. We had an account on board to buy drinks in the crew bar - $1 a beer, or full price in passenger areas, plus the on board Cambusa to buy water and any booze you want for your cabin ready for the cabin parties.

On board facilities included a crew gym, crew laundry, internet access, and there was a crew pool on board so if you had some time off you could laze in the sun by the pool. For food you could go to the crew mess or officers mess (depending on your rank). We were allowed to eat in passenger areas so we could eat in the buffet or restaurants on board. During the day we would wear khaki trousers or shorts and the company polo shirt, and blacks for backstage. Life on board is a big party. There was a crew disco each cruise, and most nights we would be in the bar or at a spontaneous cabin party.

I lived in a cabin that I shared with one other person. There were single bunk beds, a TV, a fridge, a desk and an en-suite with a toilet, sink and shower. It is fun sharing. Most of the time I got along really well with my cabin mates and am still friends with a lot of them now.

It is an amazing experience working on a ship. You make some amazing friends and get paid to see the world, as well as enjoying the wide range of work you do on board which enables you to get a good experience in a range of areas in theatre such as sound, lighting, automation and Production Management. A lot of people I know that joined as stage crew found themselves drawn to a particular area of the theatre and used their time to get more experience, get promoted on board and then leave the ships to enter the industry with a wider knowledge of their chosen area. I would never have imagined that I would end up in Automation until I got on ships and discovered that's what I wanted to do.

After four years on ships I decided that it was time to leave. Although I had a fantastic time four years was enough. Just after I made that decision I went to a Cirque Du Soleil 'Red Curtain Event' at the Royal Albert Hall. The Cirque Red Curtain events are an opportunity to go backstage and meet people from each department backstage. I signed up for a general interview in London, which was so they could get an idea of my experience. I was then called for a formal phone interview and was offered a job with the Cirque Du Soleil show 'Zaia'. I couldn't believe I was moving to Macau, which is an hour from Hong Kong.

The flights and insurance were all covered by the company. I had two weeks in a hotel to find an apartment and found myself a gorgeous furnished apartment. Living in Macau was a fantastic experience. It is hot and humid, there are typhoons, and winter lasts for two months, then it's hot and humid again. The lifestyle there is great. There are some lovely pools to laze by, and there are some gorgeous parts of the island and it was great popping to Hong Kong for some shopping or a night out, as it was only an hour on the ferry. It was interesting when it came to the language. Cantonese is a really hard language to learn and after three and a half years I knew enough to get by, but that wasn't a lot. It was easy to get by on the little that I learnt.

I loved working with Cirque Du Soleil. Zaia was a huge show and the Automation was amazing. We were a department of 11. My experience had been predominantly as an automation operator so I learned a lot at Zaia. We did all the maintenance of the equipment, the setting up and tear down of training sessions, and I was on a rotation operating the three automation boards during the show. We did programming for new sections of the show on a regular basis.

I decided it was time to leave Macau as I had been there for three and a half years so I returned to the UK and I am now working with the Royal Shakespeare Company in Stratford Upon Avon. It was quite interesting moving from China to one of the most English parts of England. Who knows where I'll end up next...

Working abroad is an amazing experience. You get paid to see the world and meet some amazing people on the way, all while doing a job you love.

Jenni Morris now works for in the Automation Department with the RSC in Stratford-upon-Avon.

Sam Beech – Cruise Ships

Throughout the 6 years that I worked on Cruise ships, I had some of the best times of my life, made some of the best friends I have ever made and led a playboy lifestyle matched only by James Bond himself. (At least 2 of the previous statements are true..) I was also able to progress my career in directions that might not have been so easily accessible on land at a relatively vast rate of knots (no maritime based pun intended).

There are many exaggerated fables, rumours and horror stories pertaining to work on ships and some of them might perhaps contain an ounce of truth. I can write based on my experience as (at various points) a General Tech/ Sound Engineer/ Lighting Engineer/ Production Manager with Cunard, Princess Cruises and Island Cruises.

To go with the obvious format, I want to outline some of the advantages and disadvantages as I experienced them.

Travel

First and foremost! Ships give you an excellent opportunity to travel the world at someone else's expense and, even better, get paid for it. Throughout my career I visited Brazil, most of the Mediterranean, the Far East, the South Pacific, the Baltic, Scandinavia, Australia, the Caribbean, the USA, Canada, Africa, Alaska and a whole load of other places that I have probably forgotten all about. In my experience, I almost always had time to get off the ship and visit any ports I wanted to see, so don't imagine that you are locked in a dark steel shell for 6 months at a time.

Social Life

An extremely unique micro culture exists on ships that I have no doubt some day someone somewhere will do an extremely interesting sociological study on. It is not for the faint hearted and very much what you make of it. The population is a giant melting pot of nationalities, none of which particularly dominate. The result is a surreal multi-cultural experience that simply doesn't exist anywhere else. (Although, it very much should!) Working and living with people from such a wide range of nationalities will expose you to many different attitudes and approaches to work (and indeed life).

Work

As a theatre tech/ events type (whatever your discipline) there are often some great toys to play with. This varies from ship to ship depending on the line itself, but it gave me the opportunity to use various bits of state of the art equipment on a regular basis. Often, I would be lighting a different show every night, which is great for getting your programming chops together, be it on a ETC Expression or a GrandMA. Sound-wise, it will be a different act/ show every night, sometimes with a live band, sometimes with track. My point is that there is enough variety there to keep you amused for a while. Despite getting a bad rap, cruise ship entertainment is often of a reasonable quality and the theatres are often considerably better and more up to date than the crumbling regional theatres (or indeed West End theatres) that many will be used to. Oh, and most importantly...

Money

Is generally paid in cash at the end of each month. It is tax free (!!) and as there is no accommodation to pay for and no food (bar the odd trip to some little restaurant that overlooks the sea on some tropical island or other) it is all pretty much expendable income for saving/drinking.

Drinking

A word of warning... Alcohol is extremely cheap on a ship and the bar is open every night. Use this advice how you will, but do bear in mind that even if something is extremely cheap, when bought in vast quantities it can become quite expensive.

Lifestyle

It is certainly not ideal for a family person. A contract is generally between 6 and 8 months (going on longer). If it turns into a more permanent arrangement, you will spend about a month a year at home/ off the ship. You will work 7 days a week and will work bank holidays/ Christmas/ New Year/ etc. Whilst this may sound horrific, it really isn't that bad and there will be ample opportunity to leave the ship and only work part days. However, it is far from being a union run environment. You will need to be happy to play along with and stomach the Americanisms and "Have a nice day" attitude (at least when you are in passenger earshot).

Extra Duties

You will be given an emergency duty and it will be part of your job to ensure that you know what you are

"It is certainly not ideal for a family person. A contract is generally between 6 and 8 months (going on longer)"

doing in the event of an emergency. You will be given full training to the extent that it will bore you to tears, but it does mean that in a real emergency situation, all crew and passengers tend to be evacuated safely and without incident.

Seasickness
Port and Brandy cures all. You'll be fine.

One final bit of advice I would offer is that if you are serious about it, don't go through an agent, but apply to the lines directly. An agent will either take your money or take a cut of your pay by negotiating lower wages with you. The lines do hire directly and it is by far the best route in. Most will have a route in via their website. Like most places, if you have any friends or contacts who already work on ships/ have worked on ships, this will help.

All in all, I look back on my time on ships as a positive experience both personally and professionally. Being paid to travel sounds like a dream come true. It can be and certainly was that dream for me. One day I felt I had to wake up, before I found I'd spent my whole life asleep. However, it was certainly something to enjoy and savour whilst it lasted.

Sam Beech now works as Production Manager for Westfield Industry Award Winning Event Department.

Glossary

Here's a rundown of the technical terms and jargon we use in this book:

ACOUSTICS
A term used to describe how well sound is transmitted in a space. If a space is described as having good acoustics, that usually means that sound carries well in that space.

AM DRAM
(Colloquial.) Am dram is short for 'amateur dramatics' – i.e. theatre groups consisting of amateur performers and crew.

AUDIO
Audio can also be used to mean 'sound', or to describe things related to sound.

AUTOMATION
The use of non-manually (usually electrically) powered machinery to move stage components.

BACKDROP
The scenery at the back of the stage, or the rear curtain on a stage.

BACKSTAGE
All the areas of the theatre that are not accessible to or visible to the audience.

BOX OFFICE
The department of the theatre that deals with the audience, primarily responsible for selling tickets. The box office may also be a physical section of the theatre where tickets can be bought.

CASTING SESSIONS
Sessions held in which actors are called in to audition for theatrical roles. They will usually perform something – either a section of the script, or a monologue of their own choosing – and may have to sing or dance if this is relevant to the production that they are auditioning for. Casting sessions may be attended by a number of people – the casting director, director, producer, music director, or other members of the theatre company.

CHARACTER LISTS
Lists of the characters in a production, put together by the casting director as part of the process of organising the casting of roles.

CUE
An action or line, on- or off-stage, prompting an action by backstage crew, eg, a sound effect, or a line by an actor.

The Theatre Industry

DE-RIG
Removing the lighting and technical effects that have been set up for a specific performance, usually if a theatre company is moving to another venue, or if one show has come to an end and the theatre is being cleared in preparation for the next.

DIGS
(Colloquial.) Accommodation. Theatre digs are places where actors and crew stay while on tour, and uni digs are where students live while at university.

FIT-UPS/GET INS
Putting in lights, scenery, and other equipment, in preparation for a production

FRONT OF HOUSE (FOH)
The areas of a theatre that can be accessed by the audience.

GET OUTS
The process of dismantling and removing the lights, scenery, and other equipment after a production is over.

LX
Electrics or lighting. The LX department is responsible for lighting and electrics.

LX DESK (ELECTRONICS BOARD)
The LX desk is used to programme, operate and control the lighting components.

LIGHTING PLOT
The lighting plot is a diagram detailing where lighting components are, what colour they are, how they are focused, and other, similar details, in order to make clear the lighting design.

MARKETING
The processes and department involved in advertising a production or venue.

MIXING (SOUND)
Balancing the various sound outputs in a theatre production, so that performers can be heard, but any accompanying music or background sound is also audible. Sound mixing can also mean the editing of recorded or synthesised sound, if sounds are being created for the production.

NETWORKING
Making contacts in the industry. Sometimes special networking events are held for this very purpose, but it can as much refer to being sociable and getting to know the other members of a crew – you never know where they'll end up working next.

PATTERN (COSTUME)
The design and measurements used to make a garment to be worn by a character onstage.

PLACEMENT (COURSES)
A period of time spent working with a professional company in the industry, often arranged as a part of a college or university course.

PRODUCING THEATRE
A theatre that develops its own productions.

PRODUCTION MEETING
A meeting, or set of regular meetings, that takes place in the lead-up to a show – or throughout the run – to discuss progress, iron out issues and give a forum for different departments to meet and chat through any problems.

PROPPING (PROPS, PROPERTIES)
The term given to all the physical objects on stage.

PROSTHETICS
The term given to the make up techniques and materials that create special effects on an actor, eg, aging a performer on stage, or creating realistic monsters in film.

RECEIVING THEATRE
A theatre that programmes a series of touring productions rather than developing their own inhouse.

RIGGING (RIG)
The area above the stage where lighting, sound and other effects are fixed for use in a performance.

SCALE DRAWING
Plans for the set or scenery on paper with measurements and instructions.

SCALE MODEL
A smaller version of the full stage and set made from card, wood and plastic.

SET
Refers to the props, scenery and physical appearance of the stage.

SOUNDSCAPE
Refers to the sound effects and music for a specific production.

TECHNICAL REHEARSAL
A special rehearsal that takes place before a show opens so that the performers and backstage crew can practice running the show with all the technical cues.

VOCATIONAL
Education or study that leads to a specific career path.